interactive
SCIENCE

Butterflies do not have noses. They smell with their antennae.

Grade 3 Teacher's Edition • Chapter 2

ISBN-13: 978-0-328-61671-8
ISBN-10: 0-328-61671-0
10   16

PEARSON

Glenview, Illinois
Boston, Massachusetts
Chandler, Arizona
Upper Saddle River, New Jersey

Table of Contents

Chapter 2 Technology and the Design Process (continued)

Resource Guide

Reading

Personalized interactive learning is designed to increase comprehension

Introduce the Big Question Make Learning Meaningful

 How can Technology affect our lives?

 The Big Question Transparency

Instruct Teach Content and Skills

Students will learn the benefits of technology, the functions of machines, and the steps of the design process.

Let's Read Science! Main Idea and Details   p. 49
Vocabulary Smart Cards   pp. 69–72
Vocabulary Strategy: Make a Word Wheel!   p. 70
Academic Vocabulary: Consider   p. 70

Leveled Content Readers
    Below-Level *Designing with Technology* (Lexile Measure 500L)
    On-Level *All About Technology and Design*
    (Lexile Measure 680L)
    Advanced *Using Technology and Design* (Lexile Measure 650L)
See *Leveled Reader Teacher Guide* for Teacher Support

Lesson 1 What is technology?

Vocabulary: *technology*   pp. 50–53
My Planet Diary Discovery   p. 50

Lesson 2 What is a machine?

Vocabulary: *work • wheel and axle • wedge*
    lever • inclined plane • pulley • screw   pp. 54–59

Lesson 3 What is the design process?

Vocabulary: *design process • research • prototype*   pp. 60–65
Do the math! Read a Circle Graph   p. 64

Transfer Knowledge and Skills Assess Understanding

 How can technology affect our lives?

Build Enduring Understanding By the end of the chapter, students should be able to describe the usefulness of technology, tell about types of machines, and characterize the design process.

Study Guide   p. 73
Chapter Review   pp. 74–75
Chapter Test   pp. 75a–75b
Benchmark Practice   p. 76

Social Studies and Language Arts Connections Book

Test Prep book
    Students can prepare for sucess on standardized tests.

Inquiry · 30 Second Lab Setup!

Hands-on and minds-on learning designed to increase scientific thinking skills

Predict Why do you think the robot was designed to look like a fly? p. 47

Try It! How can you design a parachute? p. 48

Investigate It! What makes a bridge strong? pp. 66–67

Activity Card Blackline Masters
Directed Inquiry What makes a bridge strong?
Guided Inquiry How would moving the books farther apart affect the strength of the bridge?
Open Inquiry How could building a stronger bridge be explored further?

At-Home Lab Transportation in the Future p. 52

Explore It! How can a simple machine solve a problem? p. 54
At-Home Lab Complex Machines p. 58

Explore It! Which design transfers sound the best? p. 60
Go Green Salvaged Solution p. 62

Design It! What parachute design works best? pp. 78–83
Performance-Based Assessment PG p. 46
STEM Activity Book
Students communicate a problem, pose a solution, and test their solution to real-world situations as they apply science, technology, engineering, and math.

Digital · myscienceonline.com

Digital content provides flexible formats for front-of-class or individualized learning

 Untamed Science Introduce technology and the design process with an Ecogeeks video.

The Big Question Project it on your whiteboard.

Interactive Science Online Student and Teacher Editions
Vocabulary Smart Cards Hear and see vocabulary online.
Vocabulary Memory Match Practice the memory recall game.
Investigate It! Virtual Lab Perform the lab online.
my Reading Web Read leveled content.

Each online lesson has:

my planet Diary Connect to the world of science.
or
Explore It! Animation Watch the lab online.

Envision It! Assess prior knowledge.

I Will Know... Ensure students have a firm grasp of lesson concepts.

Got it? 60-Second Video Review lesson in 60 seconds.

Got it? Quiz Assess mastery of lesson content.

Writing for Science Help students meet 21st century skills.

my science coach Direct struggling students to extra practice.

Benchmark Practice Prepare students for high-stakes testing.

SuccessTracker Online customized tests

 **ExamView Assessment Suite** Choose test items from a CD-ROM.

THE BIG ?

How can technology affect our lives?

Technology

To many people, the word **technology** is synonymous with computers, telecommunications, and software. Students often assume **technology** means entertainment—TVs, DVD players, video games, and MP3 players. More generally, technology is the practical application of knowledge in a particular area. Put another way, it is the use of scientific knowledge to solve practical problems. Anything that uses information from the fields of science and math to solve problems is technology.

As described in *Science for All Americans*, (Rutherford & Ahlgren, 1991), the component of technology most closely related to scientific inquiry and to mathematical modeling is engineering, which consist of identifying a problem and designing a solution for it. Thus, science, technology, engineering, and mathematics all converge in the design process by which science and math are applied through the process of engineering to devise a general approach and then work out the smaller details.

Understanding Inclined Planes

Two of the simple machines commonly named are derivations of inclined planes. An **inclined plane** is a flat surface set at an angle.

A **wedge** is a double inclined plane that tapers to a point or sharp edge. Wedges include knives, nails, fork tines, axe heads, and even your front teeth. Wedges are also used to hold two things apart or to hold a single object in place. Carpenters used wooden wedges to level pieces of wood. A rubber wedge is sometimes used to keep a door open.

A **screw** is an inclined plane wrapped around an axis. The threads that wrap around the screw can vary in width. The farther the distance between the threads, the harder it is to turn the screw. Screws are found on jar lids and stools that spin up and down.

Understanding Wheel-and-Axles

A wheel-and-axle is not just a wheel that rotates on an axle. Instead, the wheel is fixed to the axle. In many cases, this provides a larger "handle" with which to turn the axle. A screwdriver, a doorknob, and the knobs on faucets are all examples of wheel-and-axles. In these cases, a small force applied over a large distance (the circumference of the wheel) results in a greater force applied over a small distance (the circumference of the axle). Wheel-and-axles can also work the other way, with a large force applied to the axle, resulting in a smaller force being applied over the greater circumference of the wheel.

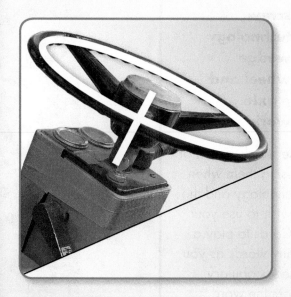

Understanding Levers and Pulleys

There are three types, or classes, of levers. They can be identified by the relative positions of the input force, the fulcrum, and the load.

1st Class Lever In a first-class lever, the fulcrum is between the input force and the load. A pry bar and a seesaw are both first class levers. A fixed pulley also works like a first-class lever, where the pulley is the fulcrum.

2nd Class Lever In a second-class lever, the load is between the fulcrum and the input force. A wheelbarrow and a nutcracker are both second-class levers.

3rd Class Lever In a third-class lever, the input is between the fulcrum and the load. Brooms, rakes, and hockey sticks are all third class levers.

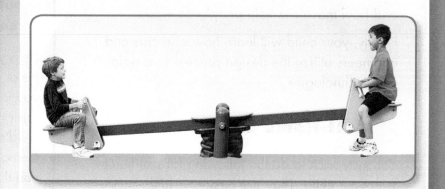

Did You Know?

The Design Process

The process presented in this text interprets the typical stages of preproduction design, which include an initial statement of design goals, analysis of those goals, research to determine if there are similar designs available, detailing the specifications of the design, documenting the evolution of the design, and presenting the solution. Production design includes testing. Post-production design includes incorporating feedback.

Chapter 2: Technology and the Design Process

Dear Parent:

After completing this chapter, your child will know that technology is applied science, and that through technology scientists help solve problems and provide solutions.

Your child will also learn about the six simple machines (wheel and axle, inclined plane, pulley, screw, wedge, and lever), how they can be combined to form complex machines, and how machines help people do work.

Finally, your child will learn how scientists and engineers utilize the design process to develop new technologies.

 ## At-Home Labs

You may wish to do the following labs at home with your child. They are easy and fun!

Transportation in the Future How might people get around in the future? Draw a picture of a tool that could help people move in the future. Write a caption for your picture.

Complex Machines Search your home for one complex machine. Draw and label the complex machine. Identify each simple machine in the complex machine.

Vocabulary Smart Cards

Your child will learn these vocabulary words:

design process	screw
inclined plane	technology
lever	wedge
prototype	wheel and
pulley	axle
research	work

Help your child make these words a part of his or her vocabulary by using them when you talk together about technology and the design process. You may wish to use your child's Vocabulary Smart Cards to play a memory game. Say as many words as you can think of to describe the vocabulary word. Have your child guess the word. Repeat using other vocabulary words, switching roles.

To learn more about *Interactive Science* and to see how your student is progressing through the program, go to **InteractiveScience.com**

Capítulo 2: Tecnología y proceso de diseño

Estimados familiares:

Después de terminar este capítulo, su niño sabrá que la tecnología se aplica en las ciencias, y que por medio de la tecnología los científicos ayudan a resolver problemas y a ofrecer soluciones.

También aprenderá cuáles son las seis máquinas simples (eje y rueda, plano inclinado, polea, tornillo, cuña y palanca), cómo pueden combinarse para formar máquinas complejas, y cómo las máquinas ayudan a las personas a realizar trabajos.

Por último, su niño aprenderá cómo investigar usando el proceso de diseño.

 Laboratorio en casa

Si lo desean, hagan las siguientes actividades de laboratorio en casa con su niño ¡Verán que fáciles y divertidas son!

El transporte del futuro ¿Cómo se imaginan que la gente se transportará en el futuro? Dibujen un aparato que crean la gente usará en el futuro para transportarse. Escriban un rótulo para su dibujo.

Máquinas complejas Busquen una máquina compleja en casa. Dibújenla y póngale un rótulo. Identifiquen las máquinas simples que hay en esa máquina compleja.

Tarjetas de vocabulario

Su niño aprenderá estas palabras de vocabulario:

cuña	proceso de
eje y rueda	diseño
investigación	prototipo
palanca	tecnología
plano inclinado	tornillo
polea	trabajo

Para ayudar a que su niño incorpore estas palabras a su vocabulario, úsenlas cuando hablen sobre tecnología y proceso de diseño. Pueden usar las tarjetas de vocabulario de su niño para jugar un juego de memoria. Digan tantas palabras como se les ocurra para describir la palabra de vocabulario. Pídanle a su niño que adivine la palabra. Repitan usando otras palabras de vocabulario y cambiando roles.

Para más información sobre *Ciencias interactivas* y para ver cómo su niño va avanzando en el programa, visiten **InteractiveScience.com**

Leveled Content Reader Support

These pages provide answers to the questions and activities on the gatefold cover for each reader.

Below-Level

Technology can help people solve problems. Scientific discoveries can lead to the development of new technologies. Simple machines are simple technologies that make work easier. In science, work is done when a force moves an object. Complex machines are made of two or more simple machines. In order to solve problems, people follow the design process.

LEXILE MEASURE 500L

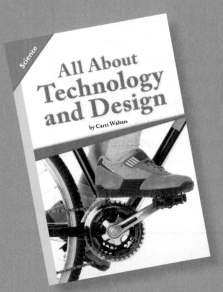

On-Level

Technology can help people solve problems. Scientific discoveries can lead to the development of new technologies. Simple machines are simple technologies that make work easier. In science, work is done when a force moves an object. Complex machines are made of two or more simple machines. In order to solve problems, people follow the design process.

LEXILE MEASURE 680L

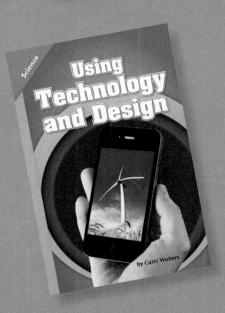

Advanced

We take many of the technologies we use every day for granted, but they all resulted from improvements made over time to earlier versions of solutions. Examples of technology a student might encounter are alarm clocks, computers, playground equipment, sports safety gear, bicycles, and automobiles.

LEXILE MEASURE 650L

Below-Level

Before Reading — ⒺⓁⓁ Principle 2

Show What You Know
Students' drawings will vary.

During Reading — ⒺⓁⓁ Principles 1 & 3

Remind students to unfold this flap as they read.

During Reading — ⒺⓁⓁ Principle 2

Do you understand?
1. Students' drawings will vary.
2. Machines make work easier.
3. People use the design process to solve problems.

After Reading — ⒺⓁⓁ Principle 5

Did you understand?
1. Possible answer: Kicking a soccer ball is work because a force moves an object across a distance.
2. Identify the problem.
3. Testing a prototype is trying it out to see if the design works the way it was meant to work.

After Reading — ⒺⓁⓁ Principle 2

Encourage students to share their airplane designs with the class.

Do the math!

1. Rock
2. 380
3. 130

ELL Support
1 Content and Language
2 Frontload the Lesson
3 Comprehensible Input
4 Language Production
5 Assess Understanding

On-Level

Before Reading   ELL Principle 2

Show What You Know

Students' drawings and questions will vary. Encourage students to record the answers they find as they read.

During Reading   ELL Principles 1 & 3

Remind students to unfold this flap as they read.

During Reading   ELL Principle 2

Do you understand?

1. Possible answers: Transportation, medical, computer
2. Machines make work easier.
3. Two or more simple machines together make up a complex machine.
4. The design process is used to solve problems.

After Reading   ELL Principle 5

Did you understand?

1. Possible answer: Kicking a soccer ball is work because a force moves an object across a distance.
2. Identify the problem; research; develop possible solutions; choose one solution; design and construct a prototype; test the prototype; communicate results; evaluate and redesign.
3. Testing a prototype is trying it out to see if the design works the way it was meant to work.
4. Answers should reflect information from the reader. Students may add additional information.

After Reading   ELL Principle 2

Encourage students to share their airplane designs with the class.

Do the math!

1. Rock
2. 380
3. 130

Advanced

Before Reading   ELL Principle 2

Show What You Know

Possible answers: Toothbrush, calculator, merry-go-round, baseball glove, lawn mower, bus

During Reading   ELL Principles 1 & 3

Use the vocabulary strategy to help students with selected vocabulary words from the reader.

During Reading   ELL Principle 2

Do you understand?

1. Technology is the use of science knowledge to invent tools and new ways of doing things.
2. They use the series of steps to find solutions for problems.
3. Identify the problem; research; develop possible solutions; choose one solution; design and construct a prototype; test the prototype; communicate results; evaluate and redesign.
4. Possible answer: Technology: clock; Improvement: Clocks without springs do not have to be wound every day.

After Reading   ELL Principle 5

Did you understand?

1. They solve the problem of holding up clothing.
2. He or she must learn what body parts need protection and how different materials can do the job.
3. Engineers design different bicycles for different uses and different riders.
4. Possible answer: Technology changes as new materials and new ways of using materials are invented.

After Reading   ELL Principle 2

Have pairs share with the class their posters detailing the development of communication technology.

Do the math!

1. Rock
2. 380
3. 130
4. Possible answer: The group of rock songs is the same size as all the other music type groups combined.

Chapter 2

Technology and the Design Process

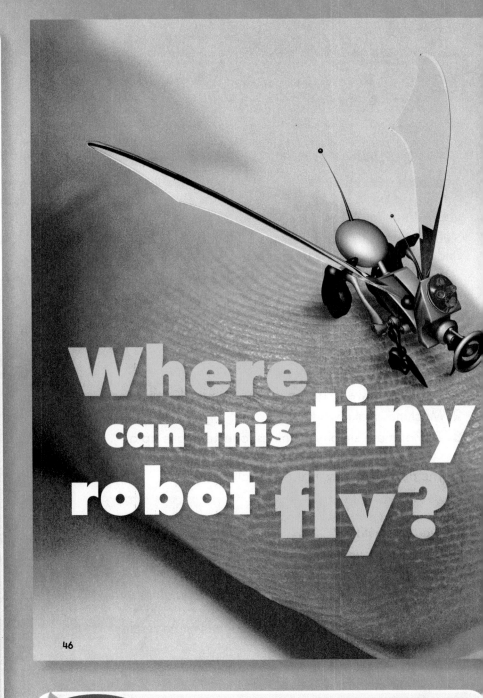

Where can this tiny robot fly?

Read Aloud: Where can this tiny robot fly?

Dr. Snider opened the door to his lab with a hearty smile on his face. He loved his work, and he especially enjoyed welcoming young people for tours.

"Come in, come in," he greeted the students. "Welcome to my wonderful world of robotics!"

The students had come for a sneak preview of one of the most amazing new robots in the scientific world, but the room they were now standing in seemed virtually empty.

Joan had been eager for the visit, imagining she would be among the first to witness a golden, human-shaped, mechanical form walking about and talking like the ones she had seen in the movies. She was disappointed to see no such figure.

Then, Dr. Snider gathered the students into a circle and slowly extended the index finger of one upturned hand into the center. Was that a bug on his finger? "My friends," proclaimed the scientist, "think of the things you could do with a machine such as this! Where can this tiny robot fly?"

▶ Predict Why do you think the robot was designed to look like a fly?

- Ask volunteers to share their predictions with the class along with the reasons for their predictions.
- Ask students to think about what the robot might be able to do in addition to flying. (Possible answer: It might be able to take and transmit pictures.)
- Read the Big Question for the chapter aloud.

Professional Development Note | **Content Refresher**

Robots A robot is a programmed, automatically guided machine that can perform tasks on its own. Contrast this definition, say, with a remote-control toy car. Though the toy is operated via radio signals that it receives as opposed to direct physical contact, the car is still "told what to do" by a person who controls its movement. A robot, on the other hand, is built with its own instructional data and can perform tasks autonomously. Among other tasks, robots can move around and they can sense and manipulate their environments. Robots are often depicted in humanoid form, but in industry, they more typically look like ordinary manufacturing equipment that is simply functioning without a human operator.

Technology and the Design Process

Chapter 2

Try It! How can you design a parachute?

Lesson 1 What is technology?

Lesson 2 What is a machine?

Lesson 3 What is the design process?

Investigate It! What makes a bridge strong?

This is an image of a piece of technology that is still being developed. Some scientists think that in the future, the robotic fly will be able to locate people who are trapped in a collapsed building. It can fit in tiny places where a person may not fit.

Predict Why do you think the robot was designed to look like a fly?

Possible answer: The robot is designed like a fly because flies are small and can move quickly.

How can technology affect our lives?

myscienceonline.com UntamedScience 47

Introduce the Big Question

How can technology affect our lives?

As you read this chapter, you will learn about technology and how we use technology every day. You will also learn how machines help make work easier for people. Finally, you will learn about the design process as you follow an engineer as he develops the first digital audio player. This information will help you understand how technology is part of our everyday lives.

How would you answer the Big Question: How can technology affect our lives?

Lesson Objectives

- **Lesson 1** Students will identify and describe ways that technology solves problems.

- **Lesson 2** Students will identify some simple machines and understand how they help people do some work.

- **Lesson 3** Students will explain how to conduct an investigation using the design process.

Inquiry

Use these labs to help students build a framework of understanding technology and the design process. Students will...

- **design** and test a parachute, p. 48

- **communicate** how a simple machine can solve a problem, p. 54

- **infer** which design works best based on testing results, p. 60

- **infer** ways to use the scientific method to improve upon a design, p. 66

Go to **myscienceonline.com** and click on:

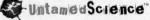 **ESPAÑOL** **CC**

Take your students on a science field trip with the Ecogeeks to see science in action.

The Big Question
Kick off each chapter by engaging your students' imagination with the Big Question.

How can you design a parachute?

Objective
Students will design parachutes that will transport a payload of one metal washer to a target with the slowest rate of descent.

Time	20 minutes
Grouping	Small groups

Materials for Small Groups

*string; *plastic bag; copy paper; *aluminum foil; *metal washer (3 cm diameter); *timer or stopwatch; scissors; *masking tape; *metric ruler

*Kit materials

Advance Preparation

Make a target on a sheet of paper. The target should be 10 cm in diameter.

What to Expect

Students will design and construct parachutes and determine which design best slows the fall of a metal washer.

Activities ⟷ Content

Students will learn about the design process in Lesson 3.

Teacher Background

Parachutes are used to slow the movement of falling objects and fast-moving objects such as race cars. The upper portion of a parachute is the canopy. A set of lines connects the canopy to the payload.

 Remind students that scientists and engineers often attempt to answer questions about technology and how it helps people by making models, observations, and measurements. Have students share with the class the data they collected for their parachutes to answer Question 5.

How can you design a parachute?

☐ 1. **Design** a parachute that will slow the fall of a metal washer dropped from a height of 2 meters.

☐ 2. **Communicate** Draw and label your design.

Possible drawing with labels

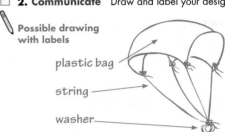

plastic bag

string

washer

☐ 3. Build your parachute. Ask your teacher to test it 3 times. **Record.** Compare your results with others.

☐ 4. Evaluate your design. Improve it. Repeat Step 3.

Parachute Trials Results			
Parachute	**Trial 1 (s)**	**Trial 2 (s)**	**Trial 3 (s)**
1	1	1	1
2	2	2	2

Explain Your Results

5. UNLOCK THE BIG ? **Communicate** Which parachute dropped most slowly?

Possible answer: The round parachute.

6. **Infer** Why did this parachute work better than the others?

Possible answer: The round parachute opened up more than the other parachutes.

48

Materials

string   plastic bag

paper   aluminum foil

metal washer

scissors   timer or stopwatch

masking tape   metric ruler

Inquiry Skill
You infer when you use your information to draw a conclusion.

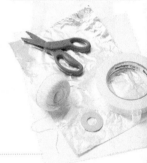

Lab Support

- Before beginning the activity, describe types of parachutes: (1) round—circular canopy; (2) square—square-shaped canopy; (3) ram-air—two layers of materials sewn together to form air-filled cells; and (4) ribbon—canopy has a hole in the center and sometimes the ring is cut into ribbons to release pressure (used for stability).

- Drop each parachute from a height of 2 meters. Students should time the descent.

Be careful! Safety Notes

- Caution students to use care when working with scissors.

- Do not allow students to drop the parachutes.

Main Idea and Details

* The **main idea** is the most important idea in a reading selection.
* Supporting **details** tell more about the main idea.

Technology and Energy

Technology has changed the way we get energy. A water-powered mill uses technology to get energy from the flowing water of a river. A solar panel can be placed on the roof of a house. It gathers energy from the sun. Energy from the wind can be captured by wind turbines. This energy helps to produce electricity. Technology allows us to recycle energy, which helps protect the environment.

Practice it!

Complete the graphic organizer below. Use it to help you list the main idea and details from the paragraph you read above.

wind turbine

Main Idea

Possible answers: New technology helps us to get energy in different ways.

A water-powered mill gets energy from flowing water.	A solar panel collects energy from the sun.	Electricity is produced with the help of a wind turbine.
Detail	**Detail**	**Detail**

myscienceonline.com | Vocabulary Smart Cards

49

Let's Read Science!

Reading Strategy

Main Idea and Details

The main idea is the most important topic that a passage is about. Details in the writing are other points that help you to better understand the main idea. Details can be descriptions or examples.

Practice It! Have students read *Technology and Energy* and fill in the graphic organizer. You may wish to have students underline the main idea and circle the details before they complete the chart at the bottom of the page.

Vocabulary Smart Cards

You may wish to have students cut out the Vocabulary Smart Cards before beginning the chapter. The cards are located at the end of the chapter in the student text.

E L L Support

3 Comprehensible Input Explain to English language learners that many paragraphs introduce the main idea at the beginning, follow with supporting details, and then conclude with a restatement of the main idea.

Paragraph structure is not limited to that order, however. Identification of the main idea can present a challenge to English language learners when the main idea is not directly stated at the beginning of a paragraph. Explain to students that it is a good idea to read and then reread a paragraph to best understand which sentence contains the main idea and which sentences provide supporting details.

Go to myscienceonline.com and click on:

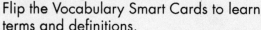

Vocabulary Memory Match
Practice vocabulary with an interactive matching game.

Vocabulary Smart Cards
Flip the Vocabulary Smart Cards to learn terms and definitions.

Lesson Plan

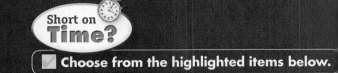
How can technology affect our lives?

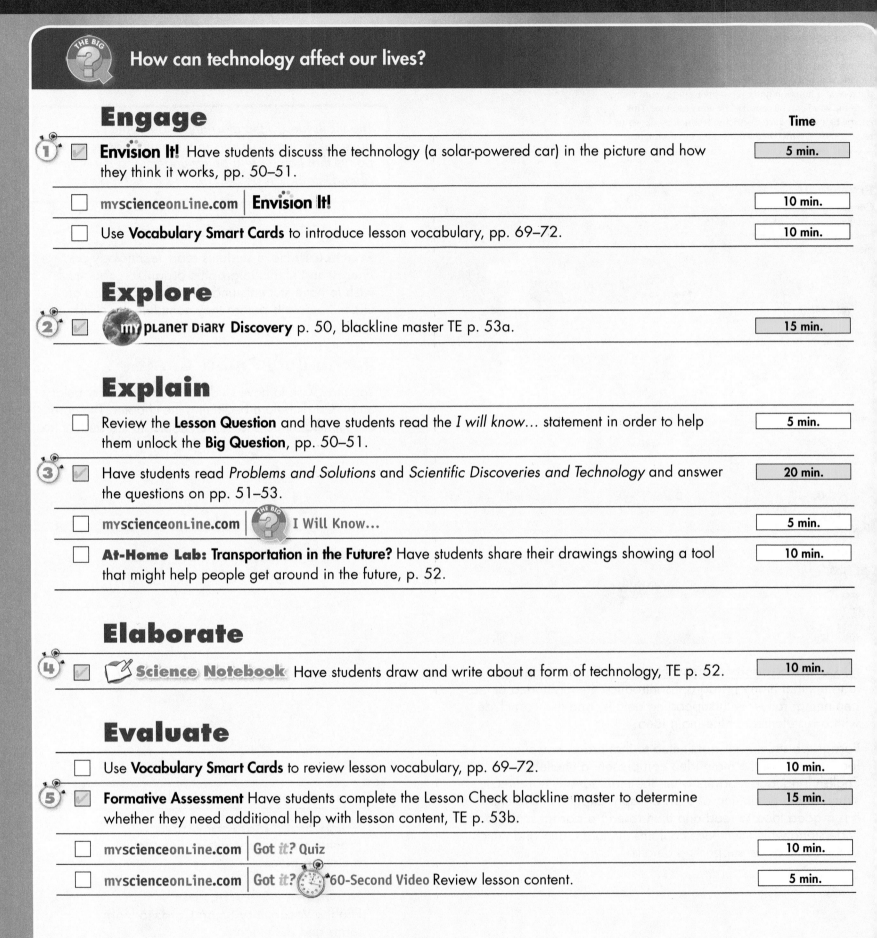

Engage

Time

1. ☑ **Envision It!** Have students discuss the technology (a solar-powered car) in the picture and how they think it works, pp. 50–51. | 5 min.

☐ myscienceonline.com | **Envision It!** | 10 min.

☐ Use **Vocabulary Smart Cards** to introduce lesson vocabulary, pp. 69–72. | 10 min.

Explore

2. ☑ my **PLANET DIARY Discovery** p. 50, blackline master TE p. 53a. | 15 min.

Explain

☐ Review the **Lesson Question** and have students read the *I will know...* statement in order to help them unlock the **Big Question**, pp. 50–51. | 5 min.

3. ☑ Have students read *Problems and Solutions* and *Scientific Discoveries and Technology* and answer the questions on pp. 51–53. | 20 min.

☐ myscienceonline.com | ? | I Will Know... | 5 min.

☐ **At-Home Lab: Transportation in the Future?** Have students share their drawings showing a tool that might help people get around in the future, p. 52. | 10 min.

Elaborate

4. ☑ **Science Notebook** Have students draw and write about a form of technology, TE p. 52. | 10 min.

Evaluate

☐ Use **Vocabulary Smart Cards** to review lesson vocabulary, pp. 69–72. | 10 min.

5. ☑ **Formative Assessment** Have students complete the Lesson Check blackline master to determine whether they need additional help with lesson content, TE p. 53b. | 15 min.

☐ myscienceonline.com | Got *it*? Quiz | 10 min.

☐ myscienceonline.com | Got *it*? 60-Second Video Review lesson content. | 5 min.

Lesson Objectives

☑ **Lesson 1** Students will identify and describe ways that technology solves problems.

☐ **Lesson 2** Students will identify some simple machines and understand how they help people do some work.

☐ **Lesson 3** Students will explain how to conduct an investigation using the design process.

Name _____ Date _____

my planet Diary   DISCOVERY

Percy Spencer's sketch helped him build the first microwave oven.

Sometimes technology becomes useful in unplanned ways. In 1946, Percy Spencer was working to improve radar. He was performing tests using microwave energy.

One day Spencer stood near the microwave energy. He noticed that a candy bar in his pocket melted. Curious, he put popcorn kernels near the microwave energy. They rapidly popped into fluffy pieces.

Spencer found that the microwave could quickly cook foods. He made a drawing that led to the first microwave oven.

Why was it important for Percy Spencer to keep asking questions after his candy bar melted?

Possible answer: Asking questions helped him invent the microwave.

Judge What characteristic of a good scientist did Percy Spencer show?

Answers will vary. Students may suggest curiosity, willingness to ask questions, good observational skills, and the ability to make inferences from observations.

Chapter 2, Lesson 1 • What is technology?
Copyright © Pearson Education, Inc., or its affiliates. All Rights Reserved.

E L L Lesson Plan

❶ **Content and Language** Pronounce the lesson vocabulary word for students. Use Vocabulary Smart Cards to provide examples, descriptions, and visuals.

❷ **Frontload the Lesson** Preview the lesson with a picture walk. Match icons, pictures, or diagrams with words or concepts.

❸ **Comprehensible Input** Present the content using visual aids, graphic organizers, and paraphrasing.

❹ **Language Production** Have students work in pairs to answer the questions that appear throughout the lesson. Encourage them to discuss each question before writing their answer in the book.

❺ **Assess Understanding** Allow students to use shortened answers for the *Got it?* self-assessment questions. Provide alternative assessment by making statements and having students indicate whether each statement is true or false by using a thumbs-up or thumbs-down gesture.

Name _____ Date _____

Words to Know
Write a sentence using the word in the box below.

[technology]

1. Sentences will vary, but students should use the word correctly.

Explain
Answer the questions on the lines below.
2. What are vaccines?
   Vaccines are medicines that protect you from disease.

3. What problem might solar energy solve?
   Solar energy might solve the problem of running out of energy sources.

Apply Concepts
4. How do you use computer technology in your life?
   Answers will vary but should include some examples of computer technology.
   _____
   _____

Chapter 2, Lesson 1 Check • What is technology?
Copyright © Pearson Education, Inc., or its affiliates. All Rights Reserved.

What is technology?

Engage

- **Activate Prior Knowledge** Call students' attention to **Envision It!** at the top of the page.

- Read the **Envision It!** instructions with students. (Possible answer: It is a solar-powered car. It uses energy from the sun to make electricity to move the car.)

- Challenge students to think about how the technology in the picture might help people.

> *How do you know something is solar powered?* (It has flat, dark panels that collect sunlight.)

Explore

- Ask students to share descriptions of how microwave ovens are used. Then ask them to tell what they know about radar. Explain that radar is now commonly used in weather forcasting, air traffic control, and police traffic enforcement.

- Read My Planet Diary with students. Ask: *How was Percy Spencer's original goal different from his unplanned discovery?* (He wanted to improve radar, but he learned that microwaves could quickly cook food.)

- Remind students that, during the steps of a scientific investigation, scientists are constantly making observations about what is going on. They look not only at the specific details they are studying, but also notice other things that happen in case they might be related.

- You may wish to have students complete the My Planet Diary blackline master.

Lesson 1

What is technology?

Envision It!

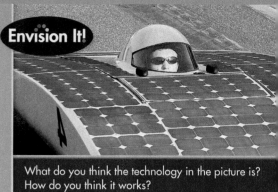

What do you think the technology in the picture is? How do you think it works?

my planet diary

DISCOVERY

Sometimes technology becomes useful in unplanned ways. In 1946, Percy Spencer was working to improve radar. He was performing tests using microwave energy.

One day Spencer stood near the microwave energy. He noticed that a candy bar in his pocket melted. Curious, he put popcorn kernels near the microwave energy. They rapidly popped into fluffy pieces.

Spencer found that the microwave energy could quickly cook foods. He made a drawing that led to the first microwave oven.

Why was it important for Percy Spencer to keep asking questions after his candy bar melted?

Possible answer: Asking questions helped him invent the microwave.

Percy Spencer's sketch helped him build the first microwave oven.

myscienceonline.com | my planet diary

50

Professional Development Note **Content Refresher**

Microwaves

- Microwaves represent a range of wavelengths of energy in the electromagnetic spectrum. Microwaves are shorter than radio waves, but longer than infrared waves (and visible light, ultraviolet radiation, X-rays, and Gamma rays).

- Microwaves at higher frequencies can heat food in a small fraction of the time that conventional heating methods take. Devices which use microwaves at lower frequencies are used in telecommunications, such as television and radio broadcasting and cell phone technology. Microwaves are also the basis upon which radar can detect the distance and speed of remote objects. Global Positioning System satellites broadcast navigational signals using microwaves.

It is a solar-powered car. It uses
energy from the sun to make
electricity to move the car.

I will know how
technology solves
problems and
provides solutions.

Word to Know

technology

Problems and Solutions

Science helps people understand the way the world works. Technology helps people solve problems and improve their lives. **Technology** is the use of science knowledge to invent tools and new ways of doing things.

Discoveries in science are helping people solve some big problems. For example, people use energy for many things. They use energy to cook food and heat their homes. But we may be running out of some energy sources. The discovery of how to use solar energy may help solve this problem. Solar energy is energy that comes directly from the sun. Solar panels gather the sun's energy. Next, they change this energy into electricity.

1. **Underline** the definition of technology.

2. CHALLENGE Solar panels work well in some places but not others. Explain why this is true.

Possible answer: Some places do not get enough sunlight.

Solar panels provide a new way of getting energy.

myscienceonLine.com | Envision It!   51

Lesson Objective

Students will identify and describe ways that technology solves problems.

Explain

 Ask a volunteer to read *I will know...* at the top of the page. Help students connect these ideas to their world. Explain that common forms of technology include cell phones and computers.

- **Build Background** Explain that some scientists answer questions, and other scientists think of ways to use those answers to develop technology, or inventions that solve problems or do work. Scientists who work with technology are often called engineers.

Draw Conclusions *If we could power our cars with solar energy, what problem would that solve?* (Possible answer: It would mean less pollution from cars because they would not burn gasoline and give off exhaust.)

Judge *What might be a problem with using solar energy to power cars?* (Possible answer: Unless there was a way to store the energy, you could not run the car in the dark.)

ELL Support

❶ **Content and Language** Students may think that technology includes only electrical devices such as computers. Explain that any tool that does work or solves a problem by applying science knowledge is technology. Share a piece of mechanical technology with students, such as blinds that use a pulley or a dead-bolt lock that uses a wheel and axle.

❷ **Frontload the Lesson** Preview the images in the lesson with a picture walk. Ask whether students are familiar with any of the technology pictured and if so, how?

❸ **Comprehensible Input** Point out or display several pieces of classroom technology, such as a computer, a calculator, and a projector. Ask students to explain what problem each piece of technology solves or how each device works. Remind students that a device as simple as a pencil is considered an example of technology.

Go to mysienceonLine.com and click on: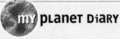

Envision It!

Find out what students already know with a few simple questions for the class.

 I Will Know...

Get to the heart of lesson content with an interactivity geared to each student's level.

my planet Diary

Learn about discoveries that affect people's everyday lives.

Explain

Have students read the information about scientific discoveries and technology. Then have students answer the questions.

Describe *What do you think life would be like if the X-ray machine had never been invented?* (Possible answer: It would be more difficult for doctors to tell whether a bone was broken, so people might not heal as well from injuries.)

Science ⟷ Social Studies

Have students interview an adult in their family about how technology has changed in his or her lifetime. Encourage students to ask about technology in the fields of transportation, medicine, and communication. Have students write summaries of their interviews.

At-Home Lab

Transportation in the Future

- Encourage students to think creatively about how people might get around in the future and what kinds of fuel vehicles might use.
- After students have finished their pictures and captions, display them on a bulletin board.

Elaborate

Science Notebook Challenge students to think of a form of technology not mentioned in the lesson that they use routinely. Have students draw a picture of the technology in their Science Notebook and write two or three sentences about how their lives would be different without it.

At-Home Lab

Transportation in the Future
How might people get around in the future? Draw a picture of a tool that could help people move in the future. Write a caption for your picture.

Signals from satellites can track the exact location of a car.

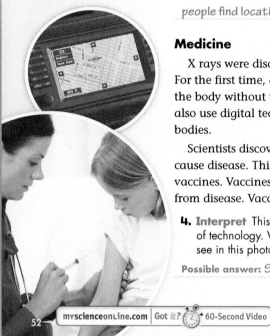

Scientific Discoveries and Technology

Scientific discoveries usually are made by scientists. Engineers use this knowledge to develop technologies that change and improve the way people live. Here are some examples.

Transportation

People on ships once had to figure out where they were by looking at stars. Now sailors can use Global Positioning System (GPS) technology. This technology relies on space satellites that send signals to Earth. Each ship's GPS computer uses the signals to figure out the ship's location.

3. ⊙ **Main Idea and Details** What is the main idea of the paragraph above?

   Possible answer: Technology has changed how people find locations.

Medicine

X rays were discovered more than 100 years ago. For the first time, doctors could look inside the body without touching it. Today, doctors also use digital technology to look inside people's bodies.

Scientists discovered that viruses and bacteria cause disease. This led to the development of vaccines. Vaccines are medicines that protect you from disease. Vaccines are a type of technology.

4. **Interpret** This child is receiving a vaccine, a type of technology. What is another technology that you see in this photograph?

   Possible answer: Syringe, needle

myscienceonline.com | Got it? | 60-Second Video

52

Differentiated Instruction

- **RTI Strategic Intervention** Have students make an illustrated list of technology they use in their homes.
- **On Level** After students compile and illustrate their lists, have them identify one item and tell a partner how life would be different *without* that technology. For example, without a washing machine, all laundry would have to be done by hand.
- **Advanced** After students compile their lists, have them identify one item that they want to learn more about. Have students use media and library resources to research the technology. Have them share their findings with the class.

Computer Technology

A computer stores information. Computers also process and send information with great speed. Computer technology is everywhere. A digital watch tells time with a computer chip. Calculators, cameras, appliances, and cars all use these chips.

Computer chips are being made smaller and smaller. Music players, game players, and phones can process as much information as whole desktop computers once could.

5. Predict How would your life be different if computer technology did not exist?

Possible answer: I couldn't play video games. I

couldn't listen to music when I'm outdoors.

Computer chips can send and receive huge numbers of electronic data signals very quickly.

Got it?

6. Give Examples Name two technologies. Tell how they have changed people's lives.

Answers will vary but may include technology such as contact lenses that help people

see or bike helmets that keep people safe.

7. ⊙ Draw Conclusions How can one technology lead to the development of other technologies?

Possible answer: New technologies make use of old technologies. For example,

computers use electricity.

⬛ **Stop!** I need help with ...... Answers will vary.

⏸ **Wait!** I have a question about ....

▶ **Go!** Now I know ....

mYscienceonLine.com | Got *it*? Quiz

53

Common Misconception

Are all computers electronic? The term *computer* refers to any device that performs calculations. Although today's computers can store tremendous amounts of data and perform many other functions besides calculations, the first computers were simple devices that did not run on electricity. The abacus is a device used for adding and subtracting, and it is constructed of moveable beads on small poles within a frame. Ancient peoples used abacuses to perform complex calculations quickly. In the 1800s, inventors developed calculating machines that were powered by steam. The forerunner of what we would think of as a modern computer was invented in Germany during World War II.

Predict *How do you think computers will change in your lifetime?* (Possible answer: They will keep getting smaller.)

Evaluate

Review Have students use their Vocabulary Smart Cards to review the vocabulary terms for this lesson.

Formative Assessment Have students answer the *Got it?* section.

Lesson Check Have students complete the Lesson Check blackline master in order to assess understanding of lesson content.

Got it?

Self-Assessment Have students answer the prompts at the bottom of the page.

⬛ **Stop!** I need help with (a concept that is still unclear).

⏸ **Wait!** I have a question about (one or two details about a concept).

▶ **Go!** Now I know (a lesson concept that has been mastered).

RTI Response to Intervention

If... students are having difficulty understanding how technology solves problems,

then... have students name a form of technology. Help them generate a list of problems it solves.

☑ **Go to mYscienceonLine.com and click on:** ⊗

Got *it*? ⏱ **60-Second Video**

Sum up your lesson in a minute.

Got *it*? **Quiz**

Test your students' grasp of lesson concepts.

 my planet Diary   DISCOVERY

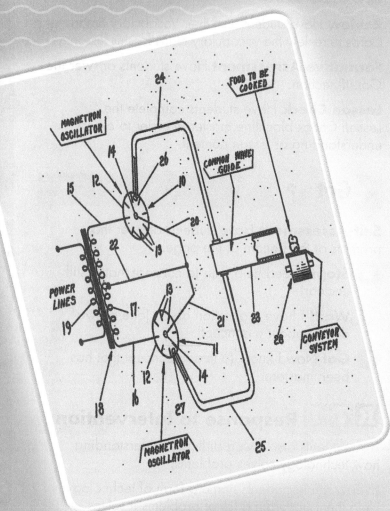

Percy Spencer's sketch
helped him build the first
microwave oven.

Sometimes technology becomes useful
in unplanned ways. In 1946, Percy
Spencer was working to improve
radar. He was performing tests using
microwave energy.

One day Spencer stood near the
microwave energy. He noticed that
a candy bar in his pocket melted.
Curious, he put popcorn kernels near the
microwave energy. They rapidly popped
into fluffy pieces.

Spencer found that the microwave
could quickly cook foods. He
made a drawing that led to the first
microwave oven.

Why was it important for Percy Spencer
to keep asking questions after his candy
bar melted?

....

....

....

Judge What characteristic of a good scientist did Percy Spencer show?

_____

_____

_____

Chapter 2, Lesson 1 • What is technology?

Words to Know

Write a sentence using the word in the box below.

technology

1. _____

_____

 # Explain

Answer the questions on the lines below.

2. What are vaccines?

_____

3. What problem might solar energy solve?

_____

_____

 # Apply Concepts

4. How do you use computer technology in your life?

_____

_____

_____

_____

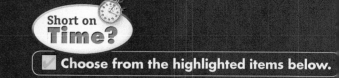

Short on Time?

☑ **Choose from the highlighted items below.**

? How can technology affect our lives?

Engage

		Time
① ☑	**Envision It!** Have students discuss how a pole helps a vaulter jump higher, pp. 54–55.	5 min.
☐	myscienceonline.com | **Envision It!**	10 min.
☐	Use **Vocabulary Smart Cards** to introduce lesson vocabulary, pp. 69–72.	10 min.

Explore

② ☑	**Explore It!** How can a simple machine solve a problem? p. 54, blackline master, TE p. 59a.	15 min.

Explain

☐	Review the **Lesson Question** and have students read the *I will know...* statement in order to help them unlock the **Big Question**, pp. 54–55.	5 min.
③ ☑	Have students read *Work, Simple Machines,* and *Complex Machines* and answer the questions on pp. 55–59.	20 min.
☐	myscienceonline.com | **?** I Will Know...	5 min.
☐	**At-Home Lab: Complex Machines** Have students share their results from drawing and labeling a complex machine, p. 58.	10 min.

Elaborate

④ ☑	✎ **Science Notebook** Have students write a paragraph describing a simple machine and its use in their everyday lives, TE p. 57.	10 min.

Evaluate

☐	Use **Vocabulary Smart Cards** to review lesson vocabulary, pp. 69–72.	10 min.
⑤ ☑	**Formative Assessment** Have students complete the Lesson Check blackline master to determine whether they need additional help with lesson content, TE p. 59b.	15 min.
☐	myscienceonline.com | Got *it*? Quiz	10 min.
☐	myscienceonline.com | Got *it*? 60-Second Video Review lesson content.	5 min.

Lesson Objectives

☐ **Lesson 1** Students will identify and describe ways that technology solves problems.

☑ **Lesson 2** Students will identify some simple machines and understand how they help people do some work.

☐ **Lesson 3** Students will explain how to conduct an investigation using the design process.

Materials ▸ Explore It!

How can a simple machine solve a problem?

- *ruler**
- *stick of clay**
- unsharpened pencil
- *metal marble**

*Kit materials

ELL Lesson Plan

❶ **Content and Language** Pronounce each of the lesson vocabulary words for students. Use Vocabulary Smart Cards to provide examples, descriptions, and visuals.

❷ **Frontload the Lesson** Preview the lesson with a picture walk. Match icons, pictures, or diagrams with words or concepts.

❸ **Comprehensible Input** Present the content using visual aids, graphic organizers, and paraphrasing.

❹ **Language Production** Have students work in pairs to answer the questions that appear throughout the lesson. Encourage them to discuss each question before writing their answer in the book.

❺ **Assess Understanding** Allow students to use shortened answers for the *Got it?* self-assessment questions. Provide alternative assessment by making statements and having students indicate whether each statement is true or false by using a thumbs-up or thumbs-down gesture.

Name_____ Date_____

Inquiry Explore It!

How can a simple machine solve a problem?
Pat and Chris want to know whose clay ball is heavier. All they have is a ruler and a pencil.

Materials
2 clay balls of different weights — unsharpened pencil
ruler

☐ 1. **Design** a way to solve this problem. Use a simple machine.

☐ 2. **Communicate** Draw your solution.

☐ 3. Test your design. Which clay ball is heavier?
The answers will vary.

Explain Your Results
4. Name the simple machine you used.
The simple machine was a lever.

5. **Draw a Conclusion** What is another way you could use your simple machine?
I could move the pencil closer to one end and

use the machine to lift an object.

What might happen if both clay balls weighed the same amount?

> Possible answer: The ruler might balance on the
> pencil, with neither clay ball being weighed down to
> touch the desk.

Name_____ Date_____

Words to Know
Write the word next to the description it matches.

work	wheel and axle	wedge	lever
inclined plane	pulley	screw	

1. <u>inclined plane</u> a ramp
2. <u>screw</u> an inclined plane wrapped around a center post
3. <u>pulley</u> a machine that changes the direction of motion of an object to which a force is applied
4. <u>lever</u> a stiff bar that rests on a support
5. <u>work</u> to use a force to move an object
6. <u>wedge</u> two slanted sides that end in a sharp edge
7. <u>wheel and axle</u> a round wheel attached to a post

Explain
Answer the question on the line below.
8. What is a complex machine?
A complex machine is two or more simple machines

that are put together.

Apply Concepts
9. Choose one simple machine. Describe how it helps people in everyday life.
Answers will vary, but students should name a simple

machine and describe how people use it.

Lesson 2

What is a machine?

Engage

- **Activate Prior Knowledge** Call students' attention to **Envision It!** at the top of the page.

- Read the **Envision It!** instructions with students. (Possible answer: The pole helps push the vaulter into the air.) Explain that the pole is being used as a simple machine. The running vaulter places the end of the pole and uses it to assist him or her to clear the crossbar.

Explore

 **Explore It!**

How can a simple machine solve a problem?

Objective Students will design a way to use a simple machine to solve a problem.

Time	15 minutes
Grouping	Small groups

Materials for Small Groups

*ruler; *stick of clay; unsharpened pencil; *metal marble

Kit materials

Alternative Materials

metal marble: any small, dense object

Advance Preparation

For each group, divide a stick of clay in half to form round balls, one with a metal marble inside.

What to Expect

If students set up their pencil and ruler like a seesaw, they can see which ball is heavier.

In this lesson, students learn about machines.

Lesson 2

What is a machine?

Envision It!

Tell how the pole helps this vaulter jump higher.

Inquiry **Explore It!**

How can a simple machine solve a problem?

Pat and Chris want to know whose clay ball is heavier. All they have is a ruler and a pencil.

☐ **1. Design** a way to solve this problem. Use a simple machine.

☐ **2. Communicate** Draw your solution.

☐ **3.** Test your design. Which clay ball is heavier?

The answers will vary.

Materials

2 clay balls of different weights | unsharpened pencil

ruler

Explain Your Results

4. Name the simple machine you used.

The simple machine was a lever.

5. Draw a Conclusion What is another way you could use your simple machine?

I could move the pencil closer to one end and use

the machine to lift an object.

54 | mysscienceonline.com | **Explore It!** Animation

Lab Support

- Be sure students understand how a lever works. To find which ball has more mass, they will need to place the clay balls at equal distances from the fulcrum (pencil).

- Have students experiment moving the fulcrum (pencil) and see how the lever works.

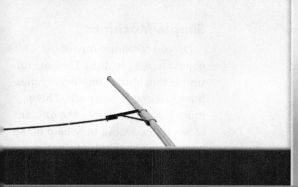

UNLOCK THE BIG ?

I will know some simple machines and how they help people do work.

Words to Know

work	inclined
wheel and axle	plane
	pulley
wedge	screw
lever	

Work

Is kicking a soccer ball work? To a scientist it is. In science, **work** means the use of a force to move an object across a distance. You do work when you rake leaves, pedal a bike, or kick a soccer ball.

It may be hard to solve a math problem. But it is not work. You may push hard to move a large rock. But it is not work if the rock does not move. You only do work when you move an object. The amount of work you do depends on how much force you use and how far you move the object.

1. **Main Idea and Details** Complete the graphic organizer below. Write details about work.

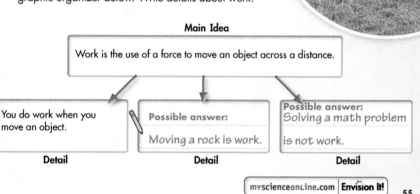

Main Idea

Work is the use of a force to move an object across a distance.

Detail	Detail	Detail
You do work when you move an object.	Possible answer: Moving a rock is work.	Possible answer: Solving a math problem is not work.

myscienceonline.com | Envision It!

55

Lesson Objective

Students will identify some simple machines and understand how they help people do work.

Inquiry **Explore It!** Students will design a way to use a simple machine to solve a problem.

Explain

 Ask a volunteer to read *I will know…* at the top of the page. Help students connect these ideas to their world.

- **Build Background** Point out to students that they use simple machines when they cut food, turn a wheel, or walk up a ramp.

> **Define** *How does a scientist define work?* (Work means to use a force to move an object.)
>
> **Summarize** *What determines the amount of work done?* (How much force is used and how far the object is moved)
>
> **Apply** *Are you doing work if you push on a door and it doesn't open? Explain why or why not.* (I am not doing work because the door did not move.)

ELL Support

1 Content and Language Write the word *work* on the board and have students say the word. Tell students that *work* has several meanings and is used as different parts of speech: *I do not have any work to do. This report was hard work.* Reinforce that the common use of the word *work* is different from its use in science.

2 Frontload the Lesson Have students read the section titles and questions, examine the illustrations and photographs, and read the captions and labels. Discuss these text features as a class.

3 Comprehensible Input Have each student make a four-column chart with the following headings: "Questions," "Work," "Simple Machines," and "Complex Machines." Before reading, have them write questions they have about these topics. As they read, students can record the answers.

 Go to **myscienceonline.com** and click on: ✕

Envision It!

Help students envision what they know about science.

 I Will Know...

Reveal core lesson content through interactivities designed to get students thinking.

Explore It! Animation

Quick and simple textbook labs come alive in a virtual environment.

Explain

Teach with Visuals Have students study the pictures of the six simple machines and read the captions. Then have them read the text and answer the questions on these pages.

Name *What are the six simple machines?* (Wheel and axle, wedge, lever, screw, pulley, inclined plane)

Compare *How are all six simple machines alike?* (They only have one or two parts and they help make work easier.)

Apply *How does an inclined plane make work easier without lessening the actual amount of work done?* (Possible answer: It allows a person to use less force to raise an object to a higher level, making the work easier. However, the object has to be moved over a longer distance, so the same amount of work is done.)

For Interactive Whiteboard Classrooms

Display the pages for *Simple Machines* on the whiteboard. Ask one volunteer to come to the board and circle a simple machine that can hold things together or raise and lower things. (Screw) Ask another volunteer to come to the board and put an X on a simple machine that is a stiff bar that rests on a support. (Lever)

Remind students that in the *Explore It!* activity, they learned how a lever works. Have students identify how the other simple machines work.

A **wheel and axle** is a round object attached to a post called an axle. Turning the wheel causes the axle to turn. The axle turns a small distance as the wheel turns a greater distance.

Simple Machines

Do you recognize any of the objects in the pictures? They are all simple machines. Simple machines have just one or two parts. These machines do not lessen the amount of work you do, but they help make work easier. Six kinds of simple machines help you do work. They are the wheel and axle, wedge, lever, inclined plane, pulley, and screw.

A **wedge** is a simple machine made from two slanted sides that end in a sharp edge. As a wedge is pushed through material such as wood or food, it cuts or splits the material.

2. Identify You want to cut a piece of cake or pie. What is the common name for the kitchen wedge you use?

 Knife

A **lever** is a stiff bar that rests on a support. A lever is used to lift and move things. When you push down on one end, the other end lifts up.

56

Common Misconception

Do simple machines allow people to do less work?
Many people believe that machines put out more work than people put in. They may not understand that machines only change the form of work people do. They allow people to use less force by moving an object a longer distance (or use more force to move an object a shorter distance), but the total amount of work required to complete the task remains unchanged.

3. Apply Look at this shape ▼. Draw an ✗ on the simple machine that has this shape. How does the shape help this machine work?

The sharp edge cuts through material.

4. Identify Which simple machine would you use for each task below?

A. Raise a flag on a pole. Pulley

B. Pry open a can of paint. Lever

C. Cut an apple. Wedge

A **screw** is an inclined plane wrapped around a center post. Screws can be used to hold things together and to raise and lower things.

5. Apply Tell how a jar lid is a screw.

The lid screws onto the jar.

A **pulley** can make work easier in two ways. It can decrease the amount of force needed to move an object. It can also change the direction that the force is applied.

An **inclined plane**, or a ramp, is a slanted surface. It connects a lower level to a higher level. Less force is needed to move an object over a longer distance.

myscienceonline.com | ? I Will Know... | 57

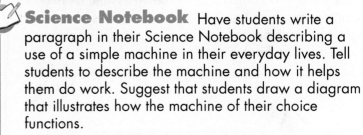

Identify *Which simple machine would you use to hold two pieces of wood together?* (I would use a screw.)

Explain *Why does pulling down on a pulley cause a force that pulls an object up?* (Possible answer: The pulley changes the direction of the force.)

Analyze *Which simple machine did the pole vaulter use in the* **Envision It!** *photo?* (A lever)

Elaborate

Science Notebook Have students write a paragraph in their Science Notebook describing a use of a simple machine in their everyday lives. Tell students to describe the machine and how it helps them do work. Suggest that students draw a diagram that illustrates how the machine of their choice functions.

Differentiated Instruction

- **RTI** **Strategic Intervention** Have students make picture note cards for the six simple machines. Provide students with index cards, and have them write the name of a simple machine and draw a picture of it on the front of a card. On the back, have students add a description of the machine and what it does.

- **On-Level** Have students work in pairs to use the cards to quiz each other. Encourage them to make a game of the exercise by identifying as many examples as they can of things they can do with simple machines.

- **Advanced** Scatter a selection of everyday simple machines throughout the classroom. Direct a student to draw a card from the six without looking. Have the student identify in the classroom an example of the machine depicted on the card and demonstrate its function.

Explain

Have students read the information on complex machines and answer the questions that follow.

List *What are three kinds of simple machines in a can opener?* (A can opener has a wheel and axle, levers, and a wedge.)

Identify *Which simple machine in a can opener actually opens the can?* (The wedge opens the can.)

Contrast *What is the difference between a simple machine and a complex machine?* (Possible answer: A simple machine has just one or two parts. A complex machine has two or more simple machines that work together.)

At-Home Lab

Complex Machines

- Materials: paper and pencil

- Review the six simple machines. Remind students to look for machines that are made of simple machines that work together.

- Suggest that students examine can openers, bicycles, scissors, staplers, wheelbarrows, and lawn mowers.

- Encourage students to pay close attention to the parts of the complex machine and to draw and label these parts accurately.

- Have students refer to the illustrations of simple machines to help them identify similar ones in their complex machines.

At-Home Lab

Complex Machines
Search your home for one complex machine. Draw and label the complex machine. Identify each simple machine in the complex machine.

Complex Machines

Simple machines are often put together to do bigger jobs. These complex machines are made up of simple machines that work together.

The can opener below is a complex machine. Find the simple machines that it is made of. These simple machines work together to grip, turn, and slice through a can lid.

The bicycle is a complex machine too. What simple machines make it up? How does each simple machine help make the bicycle work?

6. Exemplify List three complex machines that you used yesterday.

Answers will vary

but might include a

bicycle, can opener,

and stapler.

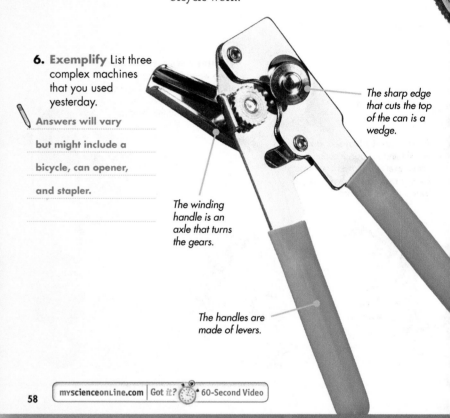

The sharp edge that cuts the top of the can is a wedge.

The winding handle is an axle that turns the gears.

The handles are made of levers.

  myscienceonline.com | Got *it*? 60-Second Video

Content Refresher
Professional Development Note

Identifying Simple Machines The simple machines that make up complex machines can be difficult to identify. This is partly because the six simple machines do not always look the same. For example, there are three classes of levers depending on where the balancing point or fulcrum is located. A seesaw, a pry bar, and a fishing pole are all levers. Also, some machines can be used for different purposes. For example, a small inclined plane could be used as a wedge.

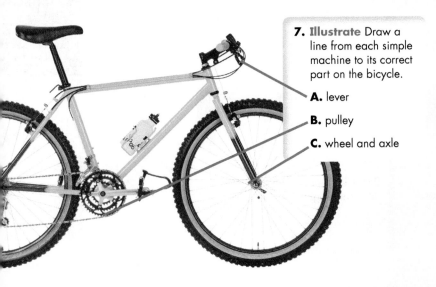

7. Illustrate Draw a line from each simple machine to its correct part on the bicycle.

A. lever

B. pulley

C. wheel and axle

Got it?

8. Synthesize How do you know when a simple machine has done work?

Something changes position.

9. Summarize Write a sentence that summarizes how simple machines are useful. Give examples.

Possible answer: A simple machine makes work easier. A lever makes it easier

to lift and move things. A screw holds things together.

Stop! I need help with ___ Answers will vary.

Wait! I have a question about ___

Go! Now I know ___

myscienceonline.com | Got *it*? Quiz

59

Information and Media Literacy Skills

Learning About the History of Machines Organize students into small groups. Have each group choose a simple or complex machine they would like to know more about. Explain that each group will become experts on their machines. They should do research in the library and online to find information such as the history of the machine, how it is used, and how it has changed. Have groups make posters to share what they have learned with the class.

Name *What are three simple machines in a bicycle?* (A bicycle has a lever, a pulley, and a wheel and axle.)

Apply *What is the job of each of the simple machines in a bicycle?* (Possible answer: The lever moves the direction the bicycle moves. The pulley moves the wheels. The wheel and axle makes the wheel turn a greater distance than a person pedals.)

Evaluate

Review Have students use the Vocabulary Smart Cards to review the vocabulary terms for this lesson.

Formative Assessment Have students answer the *Got it?* section.

Lesson Check Have students complete the Lesson Check blackline master in order to assess understanding of lesson content.

Got it?

Self-Assessment Have students answer the prompts at the bottom of the page.

Stop! I need help with (a concept that is still unclear).

Wait! I have a question about (one or two details about a concept).

Go! Now I know (a lesson concept that has been mastered).

R T I Response to Intervention

If... students are having difficulty understanding how each of the simple machines helps them do work,

then... have students review the lesson pages and then use each kind of simple machine to accomplish a simple task.

Go to **myscienceonLine.com** and click on: ✕

Got *it*? 60-Second Video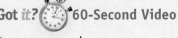

Sum up your lesson in a minute.

Got *it*? Quiz

Make sure they've "got it" with these lesson-level quizzes.

Inquiry Explore It!

How can a simple machine solve a problem?

Pat and Chris want to know whose clay ball is heavier. All they have is a ruler and a pencil.

☐ **1. Design** a way to solve this problem. Use a simple machine.

☐ **2. Communicate** Draw your solution.

☐ **3.** Test your design. Which clay ball is heavier?

Materials

2 clay balls of different weights   unsharpened pencil

ruler

Explain Your Results

4. Name the simple machine you used.

5. Draw a Conclusion What is another way you could use your simple machine?

What might happen if both clay balls weighed the same amount?

_____

_____

_____

_____

_____

Words to Know

Write the word next to the description it matches.

work	wheel and axle	wedge	lever
inclined plane	pulley	screw	

1. _____ a ramp

2. _____ an inclined plane wrapped around a center post

3. _____ a machine that changes the direction of motion of an object to which a force is applied

4. _____ a stiff bar that rests on a support

5. _____ to use a force to move an object

6. _____ two slanted sides that end in a sharp edge

7. _____ a round wheel attached to a post

Explain

Answer the question on the line below.

8. What is a complex machine?

_____

_____

Apply Concepts

9. Choose one simple machine. Describe how it helps people in everyday life.

_____

_____

_____

_____

Chapter 2, Lesson 2 Check • What is a machine?

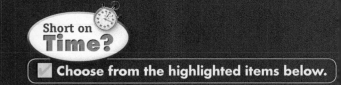

How can technology affect our lives?

Engage

Time

1 ☑ **Envision It!** Have students compare the two computers and look for differences, pp. 60–61. | **5 min.**

☐ MYSCIENCEONLINE.com | **Envision It!** | **10 min.**

☐ Use **Vocabulary Smart Cards** to introduce lesson vocabulary, pp. 69–72. | **10 min.**

Explore

2 ☑ **Explore It! Which design transfers sound the best?** p. 60, blackline master TE p. 65a. | **15 min.**

Explain

☐ Review the **Lesson Question** and have students read the *I will know...* statement in order to help them unlock the **Big Question,** pp. 60–61. | **5 min.**

3 ☑ Have students read *Design Process, Identify the Problem, Do Research, Develop Possible Solutions, Choose One Solution, Design and Construct a Prototype, Test the Prototype, Communicate Results,* and *Evaluate and Redesign* and answer the questions on pp. 61–65. | **20 min.**

☐ MYSCIENCEONLINE.com | **I Will Know...** | **5 min.**

☐ **Go Green: Salvaged Solution** Have students identify items they could salvage to build something that would solve a problem, p. 62. | **10 min.**

☐ **Do the math! Read a Circle Graph** Have students analyze data about communication technology, p. 64. | **10 min.**

Elaborate

4 ☑ **Science Notebook** Have students survey classmates and design features for a new digital audio player, TE p. 63. | **10 min.**

Evaluate

☐ Use **Vocabulary Smart Cards** to review lesson vocabulary, pp. 69–72. | **10 min.**

5 ☑ **Formative Assessment** Have students complete the Lesson Check blackline master to determine whether they need additional help with lesson content, TE p. 65b. | **10 min.**

☐ MYSCIENCEONLINE.com | **Got it? Quiz** | **10 min.**

☐ MYSCIENCEONLINE.com | **Got it? 60-Second Video** Review lesson content. | **5 min.**

Lesson Objectives

- [ ] **Lesson 1** Students will identify and describe ways that technology solves problems.

- [ ] **Lesson 2** Students will identify some simple machines and understand how they help people do some work.

- [x] **Lesson 3** Students will explain how to conduct an investigation using the design process.

Materials — Explore It!

Which design transfers sound the best?

- 2 paper cups (7 oz)
- 2 *clear plastic cups* (9 oz)*
- 2 *foam cups* (6 oz)*
- *string* (3 meters)*
- thumbtack (teacher use)

*Kit materials

ELL Lesson Plan

① Content and Language Pronounce each of the lesson vocabulary words for students. Use Vocabulary Smart Cards to provide examples, descriptions, and visuals.

② Frontload the Lesson Preview the lesson with a picture walk. Match icons, pictures, or diagrams with words or concepts.

③ Comprehensible Input Present the content using visual aids, graphic organizers, and paraphrasing.

④ Language Production Have students work in pairs to answer the questions that appear throughout the lesson. Encourage them to discuss each question before writing their answer in the book.

⑤ Assess Understanding Allow students to use shortened answers for the *Got it?* self-assessment questions. Provide alternative assessment by making statements and having students indicate whether each statement is true or false by using a thumbs-up or thumbs-down gesture.

Name_____ Date_____

Inquiry — Explore It!

Which design transfers sound the best?

Materials: 2 paper, 2 plastic, and 2 foam cups (each with a hole); string

- [ ] 1. Use 2 of the cups and 3 meters of string. Thread the string through the hole in the bottom of the cup. Make a big knot.

- [ ] 2. Test your model by talking into the cup. Have your partner listen. The string must be tight. **Record** how well you hear the sound.
  Possible answer:
  The sound I heard was faint and unclear.

- [ ] 3. Change at least one of the cups in your model. Repeat Step 2.
  Possible answer:
  The sound I heard was louder and clearer.

Explain Your Results

4. **Infer** Think about your redesign and that of others. Which material works best for transferring sound?
Possible answer: Plastic worked best.

What do you think would happen if you used a longer string?

> Possible answer: The sound would have to travel a greater distance, and I might not hear sounds as clearly as when they travel a shorter distance.

Name_____ Date_____

Words to Know
Write the word that goes with each definition.

design process	research	prototype

1. **research** to look for facts about something
2. **design process** a step-by-step method used to solve a problem
3. **prototype** the first working product that uses a design

Explain
4. What is the design process? How does it help engineers?
Possible answer: The design process is a method used to solve a problem. It helps engineers organize their information and test to see if their solutions work.

Apply Concepts
5. An engineer made a prototype of a new bike and tested it many times. Each time there was a problem with the brakes. How can the engineer use the design process to fix the prototype?
Possible answer: She could research different designs for the brakes, talk to other people, and redesign her bike.

What is the design process?

Engage

- **Activate Prior Knowledge** Call students' attention to **Envision It!** at the top of the page.

- Read the **Envision It!** directions with students. (Possible answer: The computer the children are using is smaller and easier to move.) Elaborate on the differences in the computers shown, including size and power source. Explain that the photograph on the left was taken many years ago.

Explore

 **Explore It!**

Which design transfers sound the best?

Objective Students will design model telephones to test which material best transfers sound.

Time	20 minutes
Grouping	Small groups

Materials for Small Groups

2 paper cups (7 oz); ＊string (3 meters); ＊2 clear plastic cups (9 oz); ＊2 foam cups (6 oz); thumbtack (teacher use)

＊Kit materials

Advance Preparation

- Use a thumbtack to make a hole in the bottom of each cup.

- Cut 3 meters of string for each group.

What to Expect

The hard plastic cups will transfer sound the best.

 **Activities ⇌ Content**

In this lesson, students learn how design is based on testing and evidence.

Envision It!

Tell how these two computers are different.

Inquiry | **Explore It!**

Which design transfers sound the best?

☐ **1.** Use 2 of the cups and 3 meters of string. Thread the string through the hole in the bottom of the cup. Make a big knot.

☐ **2.** Test your model by talking into the cup. Have your partner listen. The string must be tight. **Record** how well you hear the sound.
Possible answer:
The sound I heard was faint and unclear.

☐ **3.** Change at least one of the cups in your model. Repeat Step 2.
Possible answer:
The sound I heard was louder and clearer.

Explain Your Results

4. Infer Think about your redesign and that of others. Which material works best for transferring sound?
Possible answer:
Plastic worked best.

Materials

2 paper, 2 plastic, and 2 foam cups (each with a hole)

string

60 | mysout

mysscienceonline.com | **Explore It!** Animation

Lab Support

- Tell students to make large knots on the ends of the string so that the string does not pull through the holes.

- After each test, have students pull one end of the string free and snip off the knot. They can thread this free end through the new cup and knot it.

- Make sure students hold the cups so the string is taut.

UNLOCK THE BIG ?

I will know how to conduct an investigation using the design process.

Words to Know

design   prototype
 process
research

Design Process

When people design something new, they follow the steps of the design process. The **design process** is a step-by-step method used to solve a problem.

People use the design process to find a solution. A solution is an answer to a problem. The design process allows engineers to produce and test possible solutions. An engineer is any person who designs new technologies.

1. Identify Why is it important for engineers to follow the steps of the design process?

Possible answer: The
steps help engineers
find a solution to a
problem.

The Design Process

Step 1: Identify the Problem
Step 2: Do Research
Step 3: Develop Possible Solutions
Step 4: Choose One Solution
Step 5: Design and Construct a Prototype
Step 6: Test the Prototype
Step 7: Communicate Results
Step 8: Evaluate and Redesign

myscienceonLine.com | Envision It!   61

---

1 Content and Language Paraphrase the lesson objective and write it on the board. Explain each step of the design process. Have students repeat the meaning of each step.

2 Frontload the Lesson Scan the lesson headings, photos, and captions with students. Direct students to ask themselves questions about the text, such as, *What is the problem that is described in the lesson? How are the steps of the design process used?* Encourage students to write answers to their questions as they read.

3 Comprehensible Input Have students make posters illustrating the steps of the design process.

Lesson Objective

Students will explain how to conduct an investigation using the design process.

Inquiry **Explore It!** Students will design model telephones to test which material best transfers sound.

Explain

UNLOCK THE BIG ?

Ask a volunteer to read *I will know...* at the top of the page. Help students connect these ideas to their world.

• **Build Background** Discuss how new things are designed to help solve problems. For example, the telephone was designed to allow people to talk to each other from different locations. Discuss how the design of telephones has changed.

Define *What is the design process?* (The design process is a step-by-step method used to solve a problem.)

Summarize *Why do engineers use the design process?* (Engineers use the design process to help them test new ideas in order to find solutions to problems.)

 Go to **myscienceonLine.com** and click on:

Envision It!

Find out what students already know with a few simple questions for the class.

THE BIG ? **I Will Know...**

Reveal core lesson content to students through interactivities designed to get them thinking.

Explore It! Animation

Quick and simple textbook labs come alive in a virtual environment.

Explain

Have students read information on the design process and answer the questions that follow.

> **Tell** *What problem was Kane Kramer trying to solve?* (He wanted to make a music player that was small enough for people to carry and did not use tapes or records.)
>
> **Analyze** *Why do engineers sometimes research problems in different ways?* (They get different information from talking to people or reading articles.)

Salvaged Solution

- Materials: salvaged items

- Discuss some problems that might be solved by building something. Some suggestions: need to organize art supplies; desire to have a privacy screen for a desk; need to keep books, CDs, or DVDs organized or upright; need to hold a recipe card while cooking

- Have students identify what kind of items might be saved and repurposed to build their solutions.

Go Green

Salvaged Solution
Save some items instead of throwing them away. Think of a simple problem. Use the items to build something to solve your problem. Test what you build to see if it works. Evaluate your solution. Share your results with someone in your class.

People may read books to research.

2. Describe How do you think Kramer researched the problem?

Possible answer: He may have looked at older inventions such as a tape player.

Identify the Problem

Engineers identify the problem during the first step of the design process. Before producing a design, engineers consider if there is a need for it. In 1979, there were only large music players that needed tapes or records to play music. British inventor Kane Kramer identified this as a problem. Kramer wanted to design a smaller music player that did not need tapes or records. His idea led to the invention of the digital audio player.

Do Research

The next step is to research the problem. **Research** means to look for facts about something. People can research problems in different ways. Some engineers research by talking to other people and reading articles. Kramer researched ways to make a digital audio player. Kramer took notes about what he learned.

 mysienceonline.com | I Will Know...

62

Common Misconception

Is the design process really a set of steps? Like the scientific method, the design process is often presented as a series of linear steps that seem to lead logically from one to the next. In reality, both of these processes are far from linear. Emphasize that as people work through the design process, the results they get may lead them to revisit past decisions and consider many alternatives. Getting "married" to the first idea or to what is considered an elegant solution may not result in a practical solution that can be used by many people. By underscoring the steps of analysis and redesigning, students will gain a better understanding of how the design process works in the real world.

Develop Possible Solutions

After doing research, engineers think of possible solutions. They consider what designs would best meet the needs of the problem. Kramer considered different materials that were available. He knew he needed to use materials that would produce a player people would use. It had to be small enough to fit in a pocket. He made different sketches of how the player could look.

Choose One Solution

People consider many things in order to choose the best solution. They think about how they will build the solution. They also think about what kinds of materials will work. Kramer chose the best solution. His player would be made of strong materials and be small in size.

Design and Construct a Prototype

After sketching the digital audio player, Kramer constructed, or built, a prototype. A **prototype** is the first working product that uses a design. Kramer made the player small and easy to use.

Test the Prototype

Engineers test a prototype to determine if it meets their expectations. They perform multiple tests to get accurate results. Kramer tested the prototype to see how well it worked.

3. Suggest What do you think Kramer learned from his test?

Possible answer: He probably learned how well the

digital audio player worked.

car prototype

4. Determine How can this car prototype help engineers?

Possible answer:

It can help engineers

decide whether or not

the design works.

Someone may test an inner part of a computer to see how well it works.

63

Define *What is a prototype?* (A prototype is the first working product that uses a design.)

Conclude *Why was it important that Kramer's digital audio player be small and made of strong materials?* (Possible answer: He wanted it to fit in people's pockets.)

Generalize *Why do engineers test their prototypes many times?* (Possible answer: To see how well their design works)

Activities ⇄ Content

Remind students that in the *Explore It!* activity, they evaluated the effect of different materials on the transfer of sound. The same kind of thinking process would be used to evaluate materials that could make a digital audio player.

Elaborate

Science Notebook Have students think of important features in a digital audio player and list them in their Science Notebook. Then have students survey classmates, asking which features they would like in a digital audio player. Students can then plan and draw a design based on the class survey. Ask students to include a description of all the features of their new design. Allow time for students to present their designs to the class.

21st Century Learning

Communication Skills

Research Earlier Designs Organize students into small groups. Provide each group with a description and a picture of a digital audio player. Then have each group research to find earlier models of the player. As students evaluate each model, have them discuss how it changed. Have groups present their findings about each model.

Explain

Have students read the information on communicating results and evaluating and redesigning. Then have students complete the activities that follow.

Recall *Why do engineers communicate the results of their tests?* (Possible answer: They want to explain how their designs work; they want people to invest in their designs.)

Identify *Why do engineers evaluate their work?* (Possible answer: It helps them identify problems with their designs.)

Judge *An engineer designs headphones for a digital audio player. The headphones are very big and heavy. How might the engineer change the design?* (Possible answers: The engineer can use a different material that is smaller and lightweight.)

Do the math!

- Read *Do the math!* together with students.

- Explain that each color of the circle graph represents a different type of music.

What types of music does Mark have on his digital audio player? (Rock, hip hop, techno, and pop)

Which type of music is one-fourth of the total music on Mark's digital audio player? (Hip hop)

Which type of music does Mark probably like best? How do you know? (Rock; he has the most rock songs on his digital audio player.)

This is what the inside of a digital audio player looks like. Showing it to others can help them understand the design.

Communicate Results

Engineers communicate results about their tests to people working with them. Engineers n share how they designed and built the prototy They also explain how the experiment was car out. After testing it, Kramer sent a report of his invention to a group of people. He hoped the people would invest money in his invention. T report described the way his invention worked. also explained how the player could change th way people listened to music.

5. Predict What would happen if engineers did communicate their evidence with others?

Possible answer: People may not understand how to use an invention.

Do the math!

Read a Circle Graph

Mark's digital audio player can hold 1,000 songs. Look at the circle graph below. It tells you what types of music are on Mark's player and how many songs are in each type.

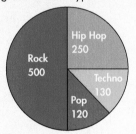

1 What type of music does Mark have the most of?

Rock music

2 How many techno and hip hop songs does Mark have?

380

3 Solve How many more hip hop songs are there than pop songs?

130

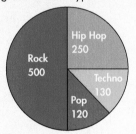

mySCIENCEONLINE.com | Got *it*? 60-Second Video

64

The Engineering Design Process

- The steps described in this lesson are part of what is known as the *engineering design process*. The engineering design process is the way in which new products are conceptualized, developed, tested, and refined.

- The engineering design process does not have one specific set of steps that must be followed each time. Instead, it's cyclical and can begin at any step.

- Scientists and engineers are dependent on each other. While doing their research, scientists use technologies that have been developed by engineers. Engineers use information from scientific research when they conceptualize their new designs.

Evaluate and Redesign

The final step is to evaluate and redesign the prototype. Evaluate means to find out how well something works. People try to make a prototype better by redesigning it. When people heard about Kramer's idea of the digital audio player, they designed their own version. The first digital audio player became available to the public in 1997. It could play about one hour of music. Newer digital audio players can hold enough music to play for more than 100 days!

6. Contrast Look at the images to the right. How has the design process changed digital audio players?

Possible answer: The digital audio player has been redesigned so that it is smaller.

Got it?

7. Infer How can the design process help someone invent something?

Possible answer: The design process could give someone helpful steps to use when making or improving a product.

8. Clarify Why is it important to test a design multiple times?

Possible answer: To make sure you get the most accurate results possible

⬛ **Stop!** I need help with Answers will vary.

⏸ **Wait!** I have a question about

▶ **Go!** Now I know

myscienceonline.com | Got *it?* Quiz

65

Science ⬌ Writing

Have students write a description of how Kramer's invention changed the way people listen to music. Encourage them to use various reference materials such as an encyclopedia or online resources. Ask students to include pictures or drawings of the different devices used to listen to music. Have students share their descriptions with the class.

Evaluate

Review Have students use their Vocabulary Smart Cards to review the vocabulary terms for this lesson.

Formative Assessment Have students answer the *Got it?* section.

Lesson Check Have students complete the Lesson Check blackline master in order to assess understanding of lesson content.

Got it?

Self Assessment Have students answer the prompts at the bottom of the page.

⬛ **Stop!** I need help with (a concept that is still unclear).

⏸ **Wait!** I have a question about (one or two details about a concept).

▶ **Go!** Now I know (a lesson concept that has been mastered).

RTI Response to Intervention

If... students are having difficulty understanding how engineers use the design process to solve problems,

then... have students outline this lesson, listing each step and summarizing how it was carried out during the development of digital audio players.

Go to **myscienceonline.com and click on:** ✕

Got *it?* ⏱ **60-Second Video**

Get all the highlights with a 60-second review of each lesson.

Got *it?* Quiz

Test your students' grasp of lesson concepts.

Inquiry Explore It!

Which design transfers sound the best?

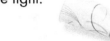

2 paper, 2 plastic, and 2 foam cups (each with a hole)

string

☐ **1.** Use 2 of the cups and 3 meters of string. Thread the string through the hole in the bottom of the cup. Make a big knot.

☐ **2.** Test your model by talking into the cup. Have your partner listen. The string must be tight. **Record** how well you hear the sound.

_____

☐ **3.** Change at least one of the cups in your model. Repeat Step 2.

Explain Your Results

4. Infer   Think about your redesign and that of others. Which material works best for transferring sound?

_____

What do you think would happen if you used a longer string?

_____
_____
_____
_____
_____

Name ______________________ Date ______________

Words to Know

Write the word that goes with each definition.

design process	research	prototype

1. ______________ to look for facts about something
2. ______________ a step-by-step method used to solve a problem
3. ______________ the first working product that uses a design

UNLOCK THE BIG ?

Explain

4. What is the design process? How does it help engineers?

____

____

____

____

____

APPLY THE BIG ?

Apply Concepts

5. An engineer made a prototype of a new bike and tested it many times. Each time there was a problem with the brakes. How can the engineer use the design process to fix the prototype?

____

____

____

____

____

What makes a bridge strong?

Objective Students will build two models of a bridge and determine which one is stronger.

Time	30 minutes
Grouping	Small groups
Activity Card	Chapter 2

30-Second Lab Setup

Have students use the laminated Lab Placemat on the Activity Card to help gather their lab supplies.

Materials for Small Groups

4 books; *metric ruler*; *10 stir sticks*; *clear tape*; *10 craft sticks*; *clear plastic cup (9 oz)*; note card (10 × 12 cm or 4 × 6 in.); 200 pennies

Kit materials

What to Expect

In this activity students build a model of the simplest kind of bridge, a beam bridge. Variables affecting the strength of each bridge include how many sticks students tape together to make each beam, how much they overlap the sticks on the beam, and how far apart they place the stick beams before gravity breaks the bridge.

Inquiry Investigate It!

What makes a bridge strong?

Follow a Procedure

☐ **1.** Place two stacks of books 25 centimeters apart.

☐ **2.** **Make a model** of a bridge between the books. Use stir sticks, tape, and a note card. Brainstorm potential solutions.

☐ **3.** Place the cup on the bridge.

Materials

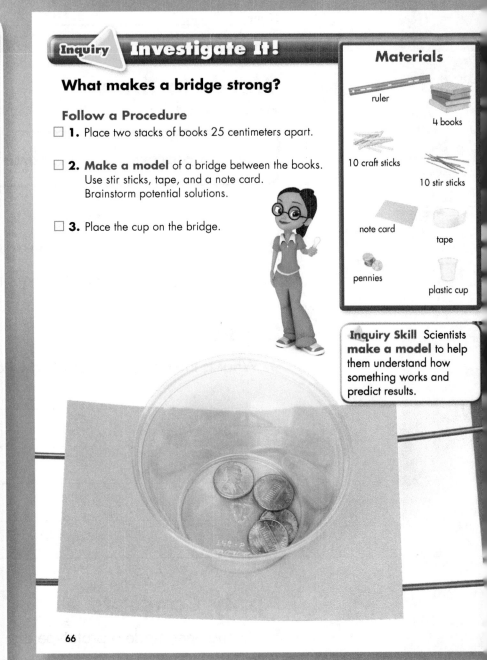

ruler

4 books

10 craft sticks

10 stir sticks

note card

tape

pennies

plastic cup

Inquiry Skill Scientists **make a model** to help them understand how something works and predict results.

Lab Support

- Make sure the books are of equal height when stacked.
- Tell students to count as they add one penny at a time.
- Have students discuss how their predictions compare with their results.
- Have groups compare their results and discuss why results may differ.

Safety Note

Tell students not to poke each other with the stir sticks or craft sticks.

4. Predict how many pennies the bridge will hold. **Record** your prediction.

5. Put pennies in the cup one at a time. Record how many pennies the bridge holds before it falls.

Sample data

Which Bridge Is Stronger?		
Model	Number of Pennies	
	Prediction	Count
Stir sticks	50	40
Craft sticks	150	198

6. Repeat Steps 2–5. Use craft sticks this time.

Analyze and Conclude

7. **Infer** How did this scientific **investigation** help you determine which bridge was stronger?

Possible answer:

I knew the bridge made from craft sticks was stronger because it held more pennies.

8. How are your **models** like real bridges? How are they different?

Possible answers:

The models are like real bridges because they cross from one high point to another. They are different because they are smaller and made of weaker materials.

myscienceonLine.com | **Investigate It!** Virtual Lab 67

 Teach for Understanding

Mention to students that scientists and engineers often build model bridges to understand how a real bridge might work. Have students work in pairs to discuss their answers to Question 7. Invite volunteers to share their answers.

Activities ⟷ Content

In this chapter, students learned how models can be used to help scientists understand and explain how something works.

Lab Hints and Tips

- Encourage group members to discuss their plans before building each bridge.

- Guide students to write an "If... then" statement such as "If we place pennies on both bridges, then the bridge made of craft sticks will hold more."

- Tell students to use their empirical evidence— their observations and data—to develop their explanations.

Inquiry Scaffolded Activities

Guided Inquiry

The second level of inquiry provides less specific procedures and requires the student to help determine the details of the procedure. Students will also devise a way to record their results. Students can refer to the *Investigate It!* activity as a model, as they answer the following question: How would moving the books farther apart affect the strength of the bridge?

Open Inquiry

The third level of inquiry asks students to pursue a question of their own choosing and develop their own procedure. A sample question might be: How would metal beams affect the strength of a bridge?

Go to myscienceonLine.com and click on:

Investigate It! Virtual Lab

Textbook labs come to life in an interactive virtual lab environment.

Activity Card Support

This activity also appears in the student text (pp. 66–67). **Materials** Directed Inquiry blackline master (TE p. 67b).

Inquiry Scaffolded Inquiry Support: **Guided**

How would moving the books farther apart affect the strength of the bridge?

Time 30 minutes

Groups Small groups

Advance Preparation none

Materials Guided Inquiry blackline master (TE p. 67c); 4 books, metric ruler, cup, pennies, and bridges made for *Investigate It!* activity "What makes a bridge strong?" (pp. 66–67)

What to Expect Students should determine that the farther apart the books are, the weaker the bridge is and the fewer pennies it will hold. This is true for both types of bridge.

Supporting Guided Inquiry

- The card gives brief instructions for this activity and does not tell students how far apart to place the books or how to record their results.

- To provide additional guidance you may wish to have students use the Guided Inquiry blackline master.

- With experience gained in the *Investigate It!* activity, students will be able to determine how to make an appropriate chart.

- Have groups compare results with each other and with their predictions. Discuss differences.

Inquiry Scaffolded Inquiry Support: **Open**

How could building a stronger bridge be explored further?

Time variable based on questions chosen

Groups variable based on questions chosen

Advance Preparation to be determined based on questions chosen

Possible Materials Open Inquiry blackline master (TE p. 67d); other materials to be determined by students, in consultation with the teacher.

Supporting Open Inquiry

- Challenge students to generate testable questions.

- To provide guidance you may wish to have students use the Open Inquiry blackline master.

- Before students begin, review their plans for feasibility and safety.

- Make sure activities use available materials. Redirect students if their activities require materials that are not available or might be dangerous.

- Give specific feedback to help improve the proposed investigation.

- Encourage students to use a suitable recording method. If necessary, assist students in creating a chart using the grid area on the Open Inquiry blackline master.

- Have students compare their predictions with their results and their results with those obtained for the stir-stick and craft-stick bridges. Then

ask students to compare their methods and results with those of other groups. Encourage them to discuss differences.

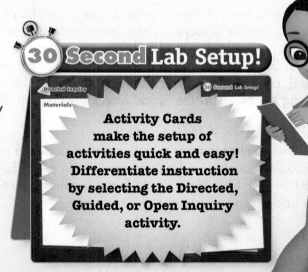

30 Second Lab Setup!

Activity Cards make the setup of activities quick and easy! Differentiate instruction by selecting the Directed, Guided, or Open Inquiry activity.

 **Directed Inquiry** **Investigate It!**

What makes a bridge strong?

4. Predict how many pennies the bridge will hold. **Record** your prediction.

5. Put pennies in the cup one at a time. Record how many pennies the bridge holds before it falls.

Which Bridge Is Stronger?		
Model	**Number of Pennies**	
	Prediction	**Count**
Stir sticks		
Craft sticks		

6. Repeat. Use craft sticks this time.

Analyze and Conclude

7. Infer   How did this scientific **investigation** help you determine which bridge was stronger?

_____

_____

_____

8. How are your **models** like real bridges? How are they different?

_____

_____

_____

_____

 **Guided Inquiry** **Modify Your Investigation**

Investigate the Question

How would moving the books farther apart affect the strength of the bridge?

1. Complete an "If… then" statement: If I move the books farther apart, then

_____

_____

2. The books were _____ apart.

3. Predict how many pennies each bridge will hold. Record your results.

Analyze and Conclude

4. Compare your observations with your predictions.

_____

5. How did the number of pennies each bridge held compare when the books were farther apart?

_____

_____

6. How does the length of a bridge affect its strength?

_____

7. How could you increase the strength of a longer bridge?

_____

Name_____ Date_____

Open Inquiry   Design Your Own Investigation

Ask Your Own Question

1. Write your question. _____

_____

Investigate Your Question

2. Materials Make a list of the things you need.   _____

_____   _____   _____   _____

_____   _____   _____   _____

3. Steps to Follow Write a plan. Write each step. Show your teacher your plan before you begin.

_____   _____

_____   _____

_____   _____

4. Observations Think of a way to record your data. Use the space below.

Analyze and Conclude

5. Tell what you learned. _____

_____

Chapter 2, Open Inquiry • Technology and the Design Process

STEM

Lawn Mowers

Activate Prior Knowledge Ask students if they have ever seen someone using a lawn mower, either in person or on television. Have students describe how the person operated the lawn mower. Also ask students to discuss what the machine looked like, and whether it produced any sounds or smells.

> *What work does using a lawn mower make easier?*
> (Cutting grass)

Summary A lawn mower is a small machine designed by engineers. It is made up of simple machines. One of these simple machines is a wheel and axle, which is used to move the lawn mower and, in some cases, to start the engine. Screws, which are used to hold lawn mower pieces together, are also simple machines.

Build Enduring Understanding

Tell students that the machines they and their families use every day, such as scissors, pencil sharpeners, bicycles, and cars, are made up of combinations of simple machines. People who build and fix these machines must understand simple machines. By learning about simple machines, students can better understand the machines they use every day.

Science
Technology
Engineering
Math

STEM

Lawn Mowers

Engineers design and develop large and small machines. These machines are made of simple and complex machines. A simple machine can be a lever, wheel and axle, pulley, wedge, inclined plane, or screw. Simple machines are often put together to make a complex machine, such as a lawn mower. It is made of different parts. Some of these parts are simple machines, such as a wheel and axle. A wheel and axle is used in a lawn mower to help it move. A screw is another simple machine. Screws are used to hold the lawn mower pieces together.

Apply Lawn mowers have wedges. A wedge is a simple machine made of two slanted sides that end in a sharp edge. Where do you think you would find a wedge inside a lawn mower?

Possible answer: The blades that cut the grass are wedges.

68

21st Century Learning

Critical Thinking and Systems Thinking Have students work in pairs. Ask them to draw a two-column chart. They should label the left column "Machine" and the right column "Work Made Easier." In the left column, students should list machines that they or members of their family use. In the right column, students should describe the work that the machine makes easier. For example, student lists may include a bicycle, which makes moving from place to place easier. You may wish to challenge some pairs to add a third column, labeled "Simple Machines," in which they list the simple machines that make up each complex machine.

Vocabulary Smart Cards

technology
work
wheel and axle
wedge
lever
inclined plane
pulley
screw
design process
research
prototype

Play a Game!

Cut out the Vocabulary Smart Cards.

Cover the words on the front of each card with sticky notes.

Use the list of words above to guess which word goes with each picture. Write the word on the sticky note.

Then remove the sticky note to see if you were correct.

69 ✂

wedge

cuña

technology

tecnología

lever

palanca

work

trabajo

inclined plane

plano inclinado

wheel and axle

eje y rueda

Vocabulary Smart Cards

Before Each Lesson Introduce content vocabulary.

- Say each word aloud and have students repeat each word.

- You may wish to have native Spanish speakers say each word in Spanish and in English.

- Ask students if they are familiar with any of the words and, if so, to provide a definition.

- Have students locate their Vocabulary Smart Cards for the lesson terms and complete the back of each card.

After Each Lesson Extend content vocabulary. Use the activities suggested for each lesson to provide additional practice using the vocabulary terms.

Play a Game!

Provide time for students to play the game. Review the directions with students.

- Cut out the Vocabulary Smart Cards.

- Cover the words on the front of each card with sticky notes.

- Use the list of words to guess which word goes with each picture. Write the word on the sticky note.

- Then remove the sticky note to see if you were correct.

ELL Support

🕓 **Language Production** Have students shuffle their Vocabulary Smart Cards and then choose two cards from the pile. Have students write a sentence that uses both of the words that were chosen. Tell students to read their sentences aloud to a partner.

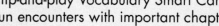

Go to **myscienceonline.com** and click on: ✕

Vocabulary Memory Match 🔊
This great practice game helps students learn vocabulary.

Vocabulary Smart Cards 🔊
Flip-and-play Vocabulary Smart Cards provide fun encounters with important chapter terms.

Interactive Vocabulary

Make a Word Wheel! Make a copy of the Word Wheel graphic organizer for each student. (See the blackline master in the *Program Guide*.) Discuss the example with students and answer any questions they may have. Have students choose a different vocabulary word and develop a Word Wheel of their own. They may use their books, dictionaries, glossaries, or other resources to help them. Note that students may not always be able to fill every spoke, depending on the vocabulary word they choose.

Academic Vocabulary

Consider is an academic vocabulary term. An academic vocabulary term is "school language." Read aloud the following text from the Lesson 3: *They consider what designs would best meet the needs of the problem. Kramer considered different materials that were available.* Tell students that *consider* means "to think carefully about." Explain that students must consider options in several stages of the design process, including when they select a solution and materials, when they evaluate the results of their tests, and when they make decisions on how to communicate and improve their solutions.

---

use of science knowledge to invent tools and new ways of doing things

Draw an example.

Possible answer: GPS, solar panel

uso del conocimiento científico para inventar instrumentos y nuevas maneras de hacer las cosas

---

two slanted sides that end in a sharp edge

Draw an example.

Drawings will vary. Check that drawings include a blade, prow, or other example of a wedge.

dos lados inclinados que terminan con un borde filoso

---

the use of a force to move an object across a distance

Write a nonexample of this word.

Possible answer:

Pushing a heavy box that does not move

uso de una fuerza para mover un objeto, por cierta distancia

---

a simple machine to lift and move things by using a stiff bar that rests on a support

List three examples of this word.

Possible answer:

Seesaw, crowbar, bottle opener

máquina simple que se usa para levantar y mover cosas mediante una barra rígida que tiene un punto de apoyo

---

a round object attached to a post

Draw and label a machine that has a wheel and axle.

Drawings will vary. Check that drawings have labels for both wheel and axle.

objeto redondo unido a una barra

---

a slanting surface that connects a lower level to a higher level

Write a synonym for this word.

Possible answer:

Ramp

superficie inclinada que conecta un nivel bajo con un nivel más alto

 70

Interactive Vocabulary

Make a Word Wheel!

Choose a vocabulary word and write it in the center of the Word Wheel graphic organizer. Write synonyms or related words on the wheel spokes.

(Word Wheel spokes: examine, test, observe, research, study, learn, inquire)

Blank Vocabulary Card

- Suggest that students use the blank vocabulary cards to write key words from the chapter that they want to remember. English language learners may find it helpful to write the words in their home language as well.

- Have students write the words on the front of the cards and draw pictures to illustrate the words.

- Ask students to write definitions of the words on the back of the cards and to use the words in sentences.

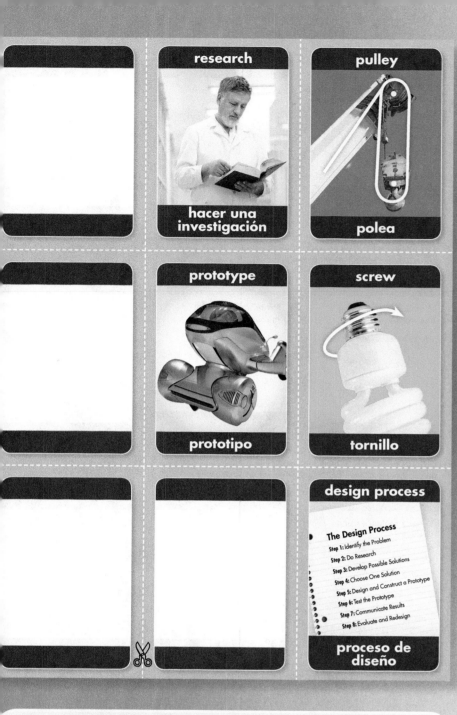

research
hacer una investigación

pulley
polea

prototype
prototipo

screw
tornillo

design process

The Design Process

Step 1: Identify the Problem

Step 2: Do Research

Step 3: Develop Possible Solutions

Step 4: Choose One Solution

Step 5: Design and Construct a Prototype

Step 6: Test the Prototype

Step 7: Communicate Results

Step 8: Evaluate and Redesign

proceso de diseño

Vocabulary Smart Cards

RTI Response to Intervention

If... students are having difficulty with vocabulary,

then... have them complete these vocabulary activities.

Lesson 1

- Have students use their card to review Lesson 1 content vocabulary: *technology*.

- Write the word on the board. Have students give examples of technology they have used so far today, either at home or at school. Examples could include things as simple as a pencil or as complex as a computer.

Lesson 2

- Have students use their cards to review Lesson 2 content vocabulary: *inclined plane, lever, pulley, screw, wedge, wheel and axle, work*.

- Have students draw a picture of a simple or complex machine. Then have them tell how the machine makes it easier to do a certain job.

Differentiated Instruction

Extra Support: Vocabulary Matching Game Have student use index cards to make a matching game that contains all of the vocabulary words. On one side of the card, have them write the word. On the other side, have them write the definition. Then invite them to play the game with a partner. They can also use two sets of Vocabulary Smart Cards to play a similar game.

Vocabulary Smart Cards

Lesson 3

- Have students use their cards to review Lesson 3 content vocabulary: *design process, prototype, research*.

- Have students draw a circle and write the term *design process* in the center. Then tell students to expand the drawing into a word web that contains words and phrases that describe the steps of the design process.

---

a machine that can change the direction or amount of force needed to move an object

What is the base word in this word?

Pull

máquina que puede cambiar la dirección o la cantidad de fuerza necesaria para mover un objeto

---

to look for facts about something

Write three examples of research.

Possible answers:

Internet search,

talking to others,

reading an article

buscar datos sobre algo

---

an inclined plane wrapped around a center post

Write a sentence using this word.

Possible answer: I used

a screw to connect

the mirror to the wall.

plano inclinado enrollado alrededor de un eje central

---

the first working product that uses a design

Write a synonym for this word.

Possible answer: Model

el primer producto que funciona y que sigue un diseño

---

a step-by-step method used to solve a problem

Write a sentence using this word.

Possible answer: The

design process helps

you construct a

prototype.

método que sigue pasos y que se usa para resolver un problema

---

Science, Engineering, and Technology

 Lesson 1

What is technology?
- Scientific discoveries can lead to the development of new technology.
- Technology can help people solve problems.

Lesson 2

What is a machine?
- In science, work is done when a force moves an object.
- Simple machines, such as pulleys, make work easier.
- Complex machines are made of two or more simple machines.

Lesson 3

What is the design process?
- The design process is a step-by-step method used to solve a problem.
- People research and develop possible solutions to problems.

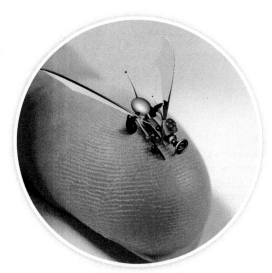

myscienceonline.com | my science COACH   73

Chapter 2 Concept Map

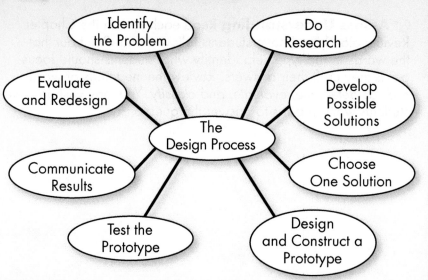

Identify the Problem

Do Research

Evaluate and Redesign

Develop Possible Solutions

The Design Process

Communicate Results

Choose One Solution

Test the Prototype

Design and Construct a Prototype

Students can create a concept map to help review the Big Question.

Teach for Understanding

Review the Big Question

How can technology affect our lives?

Have students use what they have learned from the chapter to answer the question in their own words.

How has your answer to the Big Question changed since the beginning of the chapter? What are some things you learned that caused your answer to change?

Have students make a concept map like the one shown on this page to help them organize key concepts.

APPLY THE BIG ?
Build Enduring Understanding

Think about the question "What is the design process?" Use your concept map to help you answer this question.

Go to myscienceonline.com and click on:

my science COACH

Get students back on the track to success with additional chapter activities and practice.

Chapter Review

RTI Response to Intervention

Question 2

If... students are having difficulty using the word *technology* to explain why solar panels can improve our lives,

then... direct students to review the definition of technology—the use of science knowledge to invent tools and new ways of doing things to solve problems. Have them consider how harnessing energy from the sun would improve our lives.

Question 4

If... students are having difficulty identifying a nail as a wedge,

then... direct students to review illustrations of simple machines in Lesson 2. Have them identify which tool a nail most closely resembles (the axe).

Question 6

If... students are having difficulty identifying the simple machines that make up the nail clippers,

then... direct students to first list all six simple machines, and make a simple drawing of each one. Then have them compare their drawings with the illustration of the nail clippers in order to identify the wedge and the lever.

Lesson 1
What is technology?

1. **Vocabulary** The use of science knowledge to invent new ways of doing things is called _____.
   A. scientific methods
   B. evidence
   C. a tool
   D. technology *(circled)*

2. **Write about it** Explain how solar panels can improve our lives. Use the word technology.

   Possible answer: Solar panels help conserve energy. This technology changes the sun's rays into energy we can use. We can use the energy to cook food or heat our homes.

3. **Determine** A Global Positioning System relies on signals sent from a(n) _____.
   A. space satellite *(circled)*
   B. X ray
   C. solar panel
   D. person

Lesson 2
What is a machine?

4. **Evaluate** What kind of simple tool is a nail? What is one way you could use a nail?

   Possible answer: A nail is a wedge. I could use it to fasten two pieces of wood together.

5. **Vocabulary** What machine is an inclined plane wrapped around a center post?
   A. lever
   B. pulley
   C. wedge
   D. screw *(circled)*

6. **Classify** The nail clippers are a complex machine made up of two simple machines. Label each simple machine.

lever

wedge

74

ELL Support

5 **Assess Understanding** Read each item in the Chapter Review aloud, and have students follow along. Point out that the words in red type help identify what students should focus on as they craft their answers. Review the meanings of words such as *determine*, *evaluate*, and *classify*. You may wish to have students work in pairs to answer the questions.

Lesson 3

What is the design process?

7. **Main Idea and Details**
Read the selection. Then complete
the graphic organizer.

When using the design
process, you can do research
in many ways. You can read a
newspaper. You can watch a
film. You can use the Internet. It
is important to do different kinds
of research.

Main Idea

Possible answers:

> You can research in many ways.

You can read an article.	You can watch a film.

Details   **Detail**

8. Determine After you test a
prototype, you communicate
information to other people. This
information is called _____.
A. a hypothesis
(B.) results
C. a story
D. an investigation

9.  **How can technology affect our lives?**

Think about a product you use.
How do you think it was made?
Use the vocabulary words
technology and *design process*.

Possible answer: Engineers

followed the design process

when they designed my bicycle.

They identified and researched

problems before developing

possible solutions. Engineers

used technology to build and test

early versions of my bicycle.

75

Question 7

If... students are having difficulty identifying the main
idea and details in the passage,
then... direct students to review the meaning of
main idea. Remind them that the main idea is what
a passage is mostly about. The details describe or
provide examples about the main idea. Have students
underline the main idea, and circle the supporting
details.

Question 9

If... students are having difficulty using the given
vocabulary words to explain how a product could
have been made,
then... direct students to use their Vocabulary Smart
Cards to review the definitions of the given words.
Then have them use each word in a sentence that
describes how technology is a result of the design
process.

Chapter Test Use the Chapter Test blackline master to
assess students' understanding of chapter concepts.

ExamView
Assessment Suite   Use **EXAM**VIEW® Test Prep
CD-ROM as a print or online assessment tool.

R T I Response to Intervention

If... students do not do well on the Chapter Test,

then... go to www.successtracker.com for additional
online assessment.

Fill in the bubble next to the answer choice you think is correct for each multiple choice question.

1. What is the first step of the design process?

Ⓐ Construct a prototype.
Ⓑ Identify a problem to be solved.
Ⓒ Do research.
Ⓓ Develop possible solutions.

4. What can you do with a lever?

Ⓐ lift up a box
Ⓑ hold two boards together
Ⓒ slice through an object
Ⓓ turn an axle

2. A scientist uses what he knows to modify a wedge. The new invention will help keep roads clear of ice and snow in winter. What did the scientist develop?

Ⓐ a new inquiry
Ⓑ a new design process
Ⓒ a new scientific method
Ⓓ a new technology

5. Which of the following is an example of work?

Ⓐ solving a math problem
Ⓑ pushing a rock that does not move
Ⓒ pushing on a bike pedal
Ⓓ reading a book

3. Which simple machine helps you to hold things together?

Ⓐ a screw
Ⓑ an inclined plane
Ⓒ a pulley
Ⓓ a wheel and axle

6. An inventor decides on a solution to a problem. What happens next?

Ⓐ He designs a prototype.
Ⓑ He communicates his results.
Ⓒ He redesigns the prototype.
Ⓓ He does research.

7. Identify the simple machine shown here.

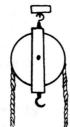

Ⓐ an inclined plane

Ⓑ a wedge

Ⓒ a pulley

Ⓓ a wheel and axle

8. Look at the picture of the scissors. What is the best description of this complex machine?

Ⓐ a wedge and a lever

Ⓑ two cutting wedges and two levers that move the wedges

Ⓒ two wedges held together by a wheel and axle

Ⓓ two inclined planes and two levers

9. Explain the steps of the process people follow to design something new.

_____

_____

_____

_____

_____

_____

10. Dave is helping his family load a moving van with boxes. He lifts up each box and places it in the van. He then climbs into the van and moves the box to the back of the truck. What simple machine could help Dave with this task?

_____

_____

_____

Benchmark Practice

RTI Response to Intervention

If... students have difficulty with these test items,

then... have students complete the test practice in the *Test Prep* book.

Choose the Right Answer Use these strategies to help students improve their scores on multiple-choice tests.

- Narrow the answer choices. Tell students to read each answer carefully. Students should rule out any choice they know is incorrect. After ruling out incorrect answers, suggest to students that they work backward from each remaining answer choice to find the best answer.

- Choose the best answer. After students mark their answer choices, tell them to reread the questions and answers to make sure their answers make sense.

Write Your Response Use the following steps to help students produce complete, well-written constructed or extended responses on tests.

- Work with students to determine what information in the visual (i.e., chart, graph, picture) they are analyzing.

- Ask students to explain the purpose of the visual they analyze.

- Explain to students that the written response should include an interpretation of the data from the visual.

- Tell students that they should also reread their answers to make sure they are complete, clear and easy to follow, and make sense.

Have students complete the Benchmark Practice questions on this page.

Benchmark Practice

Science, Engineering, and Technology

Fill in the bubble next to the answer choice you think is correct for each multiple-choice question.

1 Which technology protects people from diseases?

- Ⓐ vaccines
- Ⓑ solar panel
- Ⓒ Global Positioning System
- Ⓓ computer chip

2 What is the first step in the design process?

- Ⓐ Choose one solution.
- Ⓑ Do research.
- Ⓒ Identify the problem.
- Ⓓ Test the prototype.

3 Which simple machine is used to raise the flag on a flagpole?

- Ⓐ pulley
- Ⓑ lever
- Ⓒ inclined plane
- Ⓓ wedge

4 The first working product that uses a design is called a _____.

- Ⓐ method
- Ⓑ technology
- Ⓒ redesign
- Ⓓ prototype

5 Simple machines make doing work easier. Describe how you could use a wheel and axle.

Possible answer: When I push a shopping cart, the wheel and axle allows the cart to turn. This makes it easier to go through the grocery store aisles.

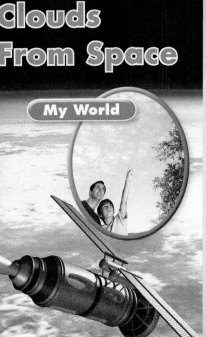

Studying Clouds From Space

BigWorld My World

My World

Big World

Did you ever lie on your back and look at the clouds? Clouds can form interesting shapes. They also can tell you things about the weather. For example, cirrus clouds are thin, feathery clouds high in the air. Cirrus clouds are a sign of fair weather. Stratus clouds cover the sky like a blanket. They often bring rain or snow.

Some scientists study clouds from space using satellites. They are trying to understand how clouds affect Earth's climate. Some satellite tools measure the sunlight that bounces off clouds. Scientists are finding that low, thick clouds reflect sunlight back into space. These clouds have a cooling effect on Earth.

Cirrus clouds are different. They allow sunlight to pass to Earth. The heat is then trapped. These clouds have a heating effect.

REVIEW What other examples of technology help people study the weather?

Possible answer: People use thermometers and computers to study the weather.

77

For next year...

BigWorld My World

Studying Clouds From Space

Read the information about how scientists study clouds with students.

Activate Prior Knowledge Ask students to share what they know about clouds—how they form, the shapes they have, and what their appearance can tell you about the weather that is on the way.

APPLY THE BIG ? **How can technology affect our lives?**

Science Notebook Ask students to summarize in their Science Notebook the technology that they believe had to be designed by engineers in order to be able to study clouds from space. Remind students that in addition to the design and construction of weather satellites themselves, there also needs to be a way to get the satellites into space and there needs to be a way for the satellites to send their information back to scientists.

Go to myscienceonline.com and click on: ✕

THE BIG ? **Benchmark Practice**

Get your students off the bench and into the game by improving performance with standards-based assessment practice.

Name_____ Date_____

▶Directed Inquiry **Investigate It!**

What makes a bridge strong?

4. Predict how many pennies the bridge will hold. **Record** your prediction.

5. Put pennies in the cup one at a time. Record how many pennies the bridge holds before it falls.

Which Bridge Is Stronger?		
Model	Sample data Number of Pennies	
	Prediction	Count
Stir sticks	50	40
Craft sticks	150	198

6. Repeat. Use craft sticks this time.

Analyze and Conclude

7. Infer How did this scientific **investigation** help you determine which bridge was stronger?

Possible answer: I knew the bridge made from craft sticks was stronger because it held more pennies.

8. How are your **models** like real bridges? How are they different?

Possible answers: The models are like real bridges because they cross from one high point to another. They are different because they are smaller and made of weaker materials.

Name_____ Date_____

▲Guided Inquiry **Modify Your Investigation**

Investigate the Question

How would moving the books farther apart affect the strength of the bridge?

1. Complete an "If... then" statement: If I move the books farther apart, then

Possible answer: each bridge will be weaker and hold fewer pennies.

2. The books were _____ apart. Possible answer: 30 cm

3. Predict how many pennies each bridge will hold. Record your results.
Responses will vary.
Possible data table with sample data shown:

How Moving the Books Farther Apart Affects Bridge Strength		
Model	Number of Pennies	
	Prediction	Count
Stir sticks	30	26
Craft sticks	180	175

Analyze and Conclude

4. Compare your observations with your predictions.

My observations matched my predictions.

5. How did the number of pennies each bridge held compare when the books were farther apart?

Possible answer: Each bridge held fewer pennies when the books were farther apart.

6. How does the length of a bridge affect its strength?

The longer bridges were weaker.

7. How could you increase the strength of a longer bridge? Possible answer: You could increase the strength of a longer bridge by adding support beneath the middle of the bridge.

Name_____ Date_____

▲Open Inquiry **Design Your Own Investigation**

Ask Your Own Question

1. Write your question. Responses will vary based on student-generated questions.

Investigate Your Question

2. Materials Make a list of the things you need. _____
_____   _____   _____   _____
_____   _____   _____   _____

3. Steps to Follow Write a plan. Write each step. Show your teacher your plan before you begin.
_____   _____
_____   _____
_____   _____

4. Observations Think of a way to record your data. Use the space below.

Analyze and Conclude

5. Tell what you learned. _____
_____

Fill in the bubble next to the answer choice you think is correct for each multiple choice question.

1. What is the first step of the design process?
   - (A) Construct a prototype.
   - ● Identify a problem to be solved.
   - (C) Do research.
   - (D) Develop possible solutions.

4. What can you do with a lever?
   - ● lift up a box
   - (B) hold two boards together
   - (C) slice through an object
   - (D) turn an axle

2. A scientist uses what he knows to modify a wedge. The new invention will help keep roads clear of ice and snow in winter. What did the scientist develop?
   - (A) a new inquiry
   - (B) a new design process
   - (C) a new scientific method
   - ● a new technology

5. Which of the following is an example of work?
   - (A) solving a math problem
   - (B) pushing a rock that does not move
   - ● pushing on a bike pedal
   - (D) reading a book

3. Which simple machine helps you to hold things together?
   - ● a screw
   - (B) an inclined plane
   - (C) a pulley
   - (D) a wheel and axle

6. An inventor decides on a solution to a problem. What happens next?
   - ● He designs a prototype.
   - (B) He communicates his results.
   - (C) He redesigns the prototype.
   - (D) He does research.

---

7. Identify the simple machine shown here.
   - (A) an inclined plane
   - (B) a wedge
   - ● a pulley
   - (D) a wheel and axle

8. Look at the picture of the scissors. What is the best description of this complex machine?
   - (A) a wedge and a lever
   - ● two cutting wedges and two levers that move the wedges
   - (C) two wedges held together by a wheel and axle
   - (D) two inclined planes and two levers

9. Explain the steps of the process people follow to design something new.

Possible answer: First, they identify the problem and do research. They develop possible solutions and choose the one they think will work best. They design, construct, and test a prototype. They keep records so they can share their results with others. Finally, they evaluate their prototype and redesign it as necessary.

10. Dave is helping his family load a moving van with boxes. He lifts up each box and places it in the van. He then climbs into the van and moves the box to the back of the truck. What simple machine could help Dave with this task?

Possible answer: Dave could push the boxes up an inclined plane instead of lifting the boxes and then climbing into and out of the van.

What parachute design works best?

Objective Students will research, design, and construct a prototype of a parachute.

Materials for Small Groups

✻ string; sheet of paper; ✻ rubber ball; ✻ chenille sticks; ✻ timer or stopwatch; ✻ meterstick; ✻ 3 rubber bands; cloth; ✻ aluminum foil; ✻ masking tape; ✻ wax paper; ✻ plastic bag; ✻ plastic cup (9 oz); ✻ plastic cup (10 oz)

✻ Kit materials

What to Expect

Students will design a prototype of a parachute to drop a cup with a ball as slowly and accurately as possible to hit a small target.

❶ Identify the problem.

In this activity students are challenged to design a parachute to drop supplies from a plane to a small island without spilling the load.

- Students are asked to identify the problems that their designs will address.

- Students will come to understand certain basic design concepts and apply those concepts to the activity.

- This step is important because it informs the rest of the design process and defines how success will be measured.

What parachute design works best?

A group of people on a small island need supplies dropped off. You cannot land a plane on the island. The supplies are fragile and must be dropped slowly so they do not break when they land. The area the supplies must be dropped off at is very small. You need to design a parachute to drop the supplies for the people that need them.

Identify the problem.

☐ **1.** Identify the problems you need to solve with your **design.**

🖉 Possible answers:

The parachute has to drop the payload slowly so it does not break.

The parachute has to drop the payload accurately into a small area.

The parachute has to drop the payload straight down.

78

Plan the Lab

Time	60 minutes
Grouping	Small groups

Possible Materials

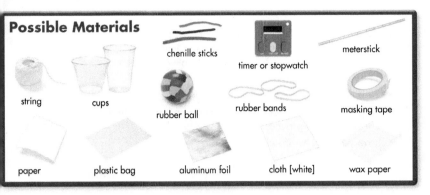

string

cups

chenille sticks

timer or stopwatch

meterstick

rubber ball

rubber bands

masking tape

paper

plastic bag

aluminum foil

cloth [white]

wax paper

Do research.

2. Think about the problems you have identified.
Research **design** solutions others have used.
Brainstorm ideas with others.
List three solutions others have used.

Possible answers:

1. A parachute was designed that dropped the payload slowly.

2. A parachute was made with a hole in the center so the payload dropped straight down.

3. A round parachute does not blow around as much as a square parachute.

Activity Notes

❷ Do research.

Have students conduct research to help them begin to formulate ideas and recognize constraints for their designs.

- Have students examine existing designs, which can provide a starting place and help students formulate questions.

- Students should discover and explore the important elements of a design, including materials usage, design constraints, and the fit of the design to the problem.

- Ask guided questions to encourage critical thinking about the problem that must be addressed in a successful design.

- As part of the research process, you may wish to have students use library resources or approved Internet sites (under your guidance).

Next, have students brainstorm possible design solutions that address the problem they identified and plan their solutions.

- Possible solutions may include variations on one design or completely different designs.

- Ask students to point out the pros and cons of each design.

- If you are using science notebooks, you may wish to have students list the steps and draw their designs in their science notebooks.

Suggest materials for the activity.

- You may wish to include other items.

- Ask students to look at the materials and decide what they will use.

③ Develop possible solutions.

Students should connect their design solutions to the materials at hand. Possibilities may include variations on one design. They also may include completely different designs.

Have students explain how each material supports their design. Some materials are better suited to solve the problem than others.

- Students should list the materials in their science notebooks for later reference.

- Suggest that students tell how each part of their design contributes to the overall design.

④ Choose one solution.

- Ask students to choose one of their proposed designs and describe it in detail.

- You may wish to suggest that students draw or diagram their design and explain why they chose it.

- Having as much information as possible about each potential solution and keeping the problem in mind will help students choose a successful design.

Develop possible solutions.

☐ **3.** Think about the problems your **design** needs to solve. Think about the solutions you researched. Use this information to draw three possible parachute designs that will solve the problems.

When you test your prototype:

- set up a target circle 50 cm in diameter.
- drop the parachute from 2 meters away from the circle and 2 meters off the ground.
- have your teacher do all three trials.

Design A	Design B

Choose one solution.

☐ **4.** Choose one design to test. Tell which design you chose. Explain your choice.

Possible answer: I chose to test the smaller parachute with the hole in the middle. My research showed that the hole lets the parachute drop down straighter. The parachute is smaller so it will not blow around in the wind as much.

80

Activity Notes

Design and construct a prototype.

5. Draw the **design** you will use to make a prototype. Label each part. Say what it is made of.

Show how your parachute design will carry the ball.

6. List the materials you used in your prototype.

Possible answers:

9 oz cup	masking tape
chenille sticks	plastic bag
string	

81

---

❺ Design and construct a prototype.

- A prototype is an original of a design.

- Explain that a successful prototype is not necessarily without problems.

- People usually change their prototypes many times before they get what they want from their design.

- Have students gather materials, build their prototypes, and explain details of their designs.

- Students should record anything that someone replicating the prototype would need to know.

Activity Notes

❻ Test the prototype.

After building their prototypes, students will have you test them.

- Testing involves assessing the prototype in terms of how well it solves the problems.

- It is important for students to understand that a successful prototype need not be perfect, but it should help the designer refine the design.

- Students should record any issues they encounter, as well as how they change their designs as they are building their prototypes.

During testing of a prototype, students record information and observations. The observations should address the parts of the design and the overall design.

- Follow the same steps each time you test students' prototypes.

- Remind students to record the results accurately. They may believe their design should function in a certain way and might modify the test results to fit preconceived ideas.

- During this step, data must be collected in an unbiased manner.

❼ Communicate results.

Sharing results is an important step in developing a final design. Have students discuss how well a particular solution worked. Students will learn from others how they approached the problem.

- Communicate test results to others to suggest possible improvements.

- The design might help other students solve problems they are having or inspire them to create a new design.

Test the Prototype

☐ **7.** Have your teacher test your **design** three times.

☐ **8. Record** the time it takes for your parachute to land.

☐ **9. Measure** the distance the payload landed from the center of the circle.

Sample data

Prototype Testing Results		
Trial	**Time to Land** (sec)	**Distance from Center of Circle** (cm)
1	2.5	40
2	2.3	52
3	2.4	10
Average	2.4	34

Communicate Results

☐ **10.** What parts of your **design** worked in your prototype? Use the results of your trials and your **observations** to support your conclusions.

Possible answers: My parachute design worked well because I was able to get it to land in the circle one time. The other two times it landed close to the circle. The data from the trials showed that my design usually landed in the same place.

☐ **11.** What parts of your design could be improved? Explain.

Possible answers: The payload (ball) came out of the cup when it landed. I could redesign the parachute so it lands in the center of the circle. I could redesign it so the payload does not fall out.

82

Activity Notes

...ate and Redesign

...hink about what did and did not work.
...Use what you learned from testing to **redesign** your prototype.
...Write or draw your design changes.

...ssible answers:

...will make the parachute bigger so it falls slower. I will redesign

the parachute so it lands in the circle all three times. I will

redesign the parachute so it lands. I will also redesign the cup

so the ball does not roll out when it lands.

83

In this last step, students evaluate the different aspects of their designs and determine why some things worked and others did not. Students will use what they learned to redesign their prototypes.

- Engage students in a discussion about their design process and results.

- Have groups compare what did and did not work, and ask them to brainstorm design changes based on shared learning.

- If time permits, you may wish to have students test their new designs.

Activity Notes